Discovering Nature Indoors

A Nature and Science
Guide to Investigations with Small Animals

Edited by
LAURENCE PRINGLE

PUBLISHED FOR THE AMERICAN MUSEUM OF NATURAL HISTORY
THE NATURAL HISTORY PRESS
GARDEN CITY, NEW YORK

DEDICATION

This book is dedicated to the people who helped make the first seven years of *Nature and Science* possible; to those who launched it, including Franklyn M. Branley, Roy A. Gallant, and Richard K. Winslow; to the magazine's staff, especially Franklyn K. Lauden and Joseph M. Sedacca; and to many steady helpers through the years, including Kenneth L. Franklin, Alice Gray, Richard M. Klein, Christopher J. Schuberth, and David Webster.

ACKNOWLEDGMENTS

The editor's thanks to the authors of the articles that make up this book; to the editorial staff of *Nature and Science,* especially Franklyn K. Lauden; to scientists at The American Museum of Natural History and other scientists, who checked the articles for accuracy; to Joseph M. Sedacca, the designer of the book; and to the artists of the Graphic Arts Department, The American Museum of Natural History, who prepared the drawings.

Mealworm Watching was adapted from the booklet *Behavior of Mealworms; Into a Gerbil's World* from *The Curious Gerbils.* Both booklets copyright © 1967 by Education Development Center, Newton, Massachusetts. The booklets were prepared by Elementary Science Study of Education Development Center. Elementary Science Study is supported by the National Science Foundation.

CONTENTS

ABOUT THIS BOOK

The planet earth is rich with living things, and humans have only begun to unravel its mysteries. There is still a lot to learn about such common creatures as ants, earthworms, minnows, and mice.

Ideally, a biologist likes to study animals outdoors, in their natural surroundings. But often that is difficult, and sometimes it is impossible. So, out of necessity, biologists bring small animals indoors and study them there.

Many of us who are not biologists do the same thing—with one important difference. We keep fish in an aquarium, or ants in an "ant farm," or even a pet gerbil in a cage. But, unlike a trained biologist, most of us don't know how to go about investigating the lives of our wild pets. We often wonder about these creatures that share our homes, but we don't know how to begin to learn about their lives. This book is designed to help solve that problem.

The text of *Discovering Nature Indoors* is made up of articles first published in *Nature and Science* magazine. Most of the articles were written by experienced biologists and naturalists. Like the magazine, this book is a blend of information, questions you might try to answer, and helpful tips on how to go about answering them.

So, if you just want to keep a goldfish, or some young turtles, or a white mouse, this book tells how to do it. If, however, you want to study the goldfish's respiration, or test the effects of different foods on the growth of those turtles, or teach your mouse some tricks, *that* information is also in this book. And if that seems tame, you will find directions for making a microscope, for training earthworms, and for investigating the life of "public insect number one"—the cockroach.

In *Discovering Nature Indoors,* you'll find an invitation to go beyond the mere "keeping" of small animal pets. Try some of the many investigations described in this book. You'll have a new appreciation of your pets. And you may gain a better understanding of all the animals—indoors and out—that share the earth with man.

LAURENCE PRINGLE

The American Museum of Natural History

Small Worlds
Under Glass

■To many people, the word "terrarium" means a miniature garden of wild plants. But a terrarium can be much more than that. It can be a small sample of a particular *habitat* (living place) where certain plants and animals are found. It can be a woodland, a meadow, a desert—any place a particular community of plants and animals lives.

You don't need much equipment to set up a terrarium. The ideal containers are those that you can see into—glass aquarium tanks, clear plastic boxes, gallon-size pickle or mayonnaise jars. For a top you will need a piece of glass, or plastic, or screening. And no matter what kind of habitat you have in your terrarium, it should have an inch-deep base of gravel so that water can drain through the soil. On top of this put two or three inches of soil. Don't leave it all level. Make a hill in one corner, or have the soil slope from back to front. Be sure you get the soil from the same place you collect the plants. Soil is a part of the habitat too.

If you plan to dig up plants from someone's land, first get the owner's permission. Since the plants you will need for the terrarium will be small ones, you can easily dig them up with a trowel or big spoon. Be sure to get a lump of soil along with the roots. To protect the plants and to keep their roots from drying out, wrap them in damp newspaper or put them in plastic bags when you dig them up. Put the plants in the terrarium as soon as possible.

Your terrarium will be especially fascinating if you have some animals in it. But too many animals, or animals of the wrong kind or size will destroy the plants. Adult turtles, toads, and frogs will crawl over and uproot plants. However, young turtles, small species of frogs, and most small lizards and salamanders do well in terrariums. Of course, a terrarium requires more care if it contains animals, since you will have to feed them.

Each living thing, whether plant or animal, must have certain conditions in order to live a healthy life. Keep this in mind when you set out to gather plants and animals for your terrarium. Mark off a four-foot by four-foot area in whatever habitat you choose—forest, meadow, or the like. Get down on your hands and knees and look for animals and the plants they live near. Look below ground, too.

Ask yourself the following questions. The answers will give you some guidelines for setting up a terrarium of the particular kind of habitat you want.

1. *What is the temperature where the animals and plants live?* Take thermometer readings in several different places on your plot of ground. If possible, do this on several different days, and at different times of the day. Take an average of all the readings. Then, once your terrarium is set up, try to keep it near the same average temperature. Unless you want desert conditions, your terrarium should not sit on a radiator or in direct sunlight.

2. *How moist is the habitat?* To answer this question dig into the soil to see how wet it is and also look at the skins of any animals you might find. Are they dry and scaly like a lizard's or wet like a salamander's?

You can control the amount of moisture in your terrarium in two ways. One way is to regulate the amount of water you put in. The other way is by the kind of top you choose for the terrarium. A screened top (or no top at all) allows water vapor to escape from the terrarium. A top of plastic or glass traps water vapor inside. By leaving such a top partly open, you can get conditions somewhere between very dry and very wet.

On the next two pages are drawings and tips for setting up four different kinds of terrariums. You may think of others to try ■

—Marlene Robinson

9

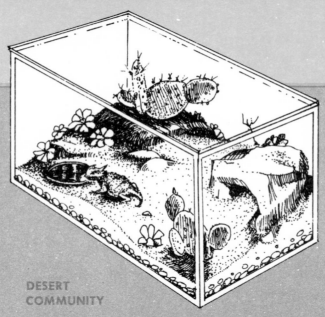

DESERT COMMUNITY

If you don't live near a desert, you'll have to get material for your desert community from places near at hand. You can get sand from a beach or garden supply store. Some kinds of desert animals, including horned lizards, can be found in pet shops. (Horned lizards are difficult to keep in captivity unless you can feed them ants. Have a sure supply of ants before trying to keep these reptiles.)

You can buy small cacti from florist shops or variety stores. Also get some *succulents*, which are plants that hold water in their fleshy leaves. Besides the plants, put some rocks in the terrarium, making cliffs or overhangs near the edges. Put a small dish of water in one corner. Leave an open area of sand in the center, especially if you have a horned lizard. (You will discover why.) The temperature should be kept between 70 and 80 degrees F.

This is the kind of habitat people most often have in a terrarium. For plants, get small ferns, tree seedlings, wildflowers, and especially evergreen plants such as partridgeberry or wintergreen. After a few of these plants are put into the soil, the rest of the surface can be covered with mosses, attractive stones, and perhaps a small limb.

For animals, look for small toads, frogs such as cricket frogs or tree frogs, and red efts (which are small salamanders). These animals and the plants of the forest floor all need moisture, so keep the terrarium well-watered and make a small woodland pool in one corner.

FOREST FLOOR COMMUNITY

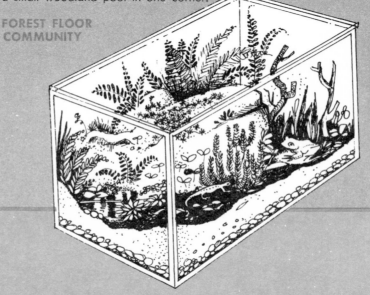

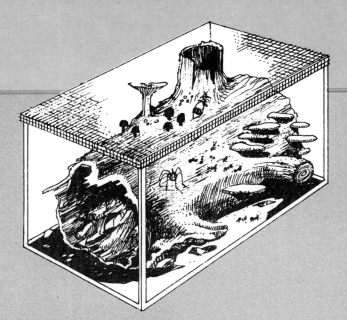

ROTTING LOG COMMUNITY

Break open a rotting log with a trowel, put two or three chunks into a plastic bag, and take them back to put in your terrarium. No soil is needed. If the log was in a damp spot, you should add water from time to time.

Many creatures may live in the log, including ants, termites, spiders, and horned beetles (sometimes called "bess" beetles because they make a squeaky hiss). If your log contains some ants, provide a few crumbs and some sugar water on a piece of sponge for them. To keep the ants from crawling out of the terrarium, spread a layer of Vaseline along the upper edge. Watch to see what kinds of insects and other animals come from the log. Some may be in the form of eggs when you collect the log and may develop into adults while in the terrarium.

The problem here is limiting yourself to a few of the many grasses, weeds, seedling trees, and other plants that grow in meadows. There are also many animals to choose from, including spiders that spin beautiful orb webs. (These spiders need lots of room, such as a 10-gallon aquarium tank, in which to make their webs.)

You may find plants with insect eggs or cocoons on them; watch to see what hatches from them. If you want to have one larger animal in the terrarium, try to find a small garter snake. It will eat earthworms and large insects. Be sure to keep the terrarium fairly dry, since snakes often get skin diseases if kept in damp surroundings.

MEADOW COMMUNITY

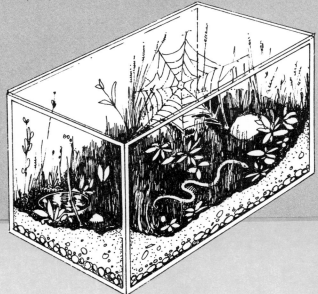

A Pond in Your Living Room

■ Keeping an aquarium is like having a miniature pond in your home. Once your aquarium is set up, you can discover many things about how water animals and plants live and grow—how a fish moves its fins, or how a tadpole slowly changes into a frog.

Part of the fun of having an aquarium is deciding what kinds of plants and animals you are going to keep in it. There are several kinds of aquariums, including ones for tropical and ocean life. A good one to try first is a fresh-water pond aquarium. Pond aquariums are inexpensive to set up and care for.

Starting Your Aquarium

To set up an aquarium you need a large glass container of some sort. A gallon jar can be used, but its curved glass causes the light to bend so that animals inside the jar will look distorted. A better kind of aquarium is a rectangular one that holds at least six to 10 gallons of water.

These tanks usually have metal frames, a slate bottom, and a removable glass top. The top is important. It keeps dust out and the fish in. You can buy such aquarium tanks at pet supply shops.

Once you have an aquarium tank, cover the bottom of it with one or two inches of fine gravel or coarse sand. (Coarse gravel traps food particles, which decay, and fine sand packs too hard to allow plants to grow.) Wash the gravel or sand (do not use soap) before you put it into the tank. Or buy

12

washed gravel at a pet shop. Otherwise the aquarium water will be dirty and unhealthy for animals. If you add some small rocks and push some of the gravel into a mound at the rear of the tank, your aquarium will have a natural appearance.

Decide where you are going to keep your aquarium before you add any water to it. A full aquarium is heavy. Moving it may damage it. Put the tank in a place that doesn't receive any direct sunlight, or too much heat.

Near a north window is best. Then fill it with water to within about an inch of the top.

You can use clear water from a pond or stream, or water from a tap. Before you pour water gently into the tank, cover the bottom with a piece of plastic, paper, or a plate so the stream of water will not move the gravel around. If you use tap water, let it stand in the tank for two or three days to allow the purifying chemicals that are added to drinking water to escape as gases into the air. Otherwise, these chemicals may poison your fish.

The aquarium is now ready for planting. You can get some small plants from a nearby pond, for example, duckweed, which is a tiny floating plant that does well in aquariums. You can experiment with others. However, the plants that are available from pet shops usually grow better than wild plants.

Some water plants—like *Vallisneria* and *Sagittaria*—have roots that must be well covered with the gravel or sand of your aquarium. Other plants— like waterweed (*Anacharis*) and water sprite—simply float in the water, although you should anchor their stems to the bottom with a small stone.

Plant the largest plants at the sides and rear of the tank. Then you will have an open area toward the front where you can easily watch the aquarium animals. Remember that the plants will grow and spread, so don't plant them too thickly.

The water may be a bit cloudy after you add the plants. Allow a few days for it to clear and the plants to begin to grow. In the meantime you can decide what animals are going to live in your aquarium.

Choosing Your Aquarium Animals

Many kinds of animals can be kept in an aquarium. They include fishes, insects, crayfish, snails, tadpoles, and salamanders (*see drawings*). You can catch many of these animals from a nearby pond (use a small dip net and carry your catch home in water-filled plastic bags), or buy them from a pet shop. Don't take animals from fast-flowing streams. They will probably die in the still water of an aquarium.

You may be tempted to put many different kinds of water animals into your tank, but some kinds of animals do not "mix" well. For example a giant water bug may catch and eat small fish, and some kinds of fish also eat other fish. If several "meat-eating" animals are put in an aquarium, only one or two may be left after a little while. If you want your animals to last, choose animals of a type and size that will not try to feed on each other.

Before you add an animal to the aquarium, be sure that the water temperature of the animal's carrier-container is nearly the same as the water in the aquarium. One way to do this is to float the container in the tank for a half-hour. Otherwise, the shock of a sudden temperature change may kill the animal.

From time to time, you may have to add some water to the aquarium to

14

ANIMALS FOR YOUR POND AQUARIUM

Here is a list of some common animals that do well in aquariums, and some tips on how to care for them.

Small wild fish—like minnows, catfish, sunfish, suckers, and shiners—are interesting and active aquarium animals. Sunfish and some kinds of minnows do not mix well with other fish. They are fine if you want a single type in your aquarium, or if you make sure they are smaller than the other fish. Some good combinations are catfish and shiners, or catfish and black-nosed dace (a kind of minnow).

Water insects—like beetles, water boatmen, and dragonfly nymphs—are easy to catch with a small net or a kitchen strainer. Many of these water insects prey on other animals, and on each other. But some people find water insects so fascinating that they keep them in aquariums so they can watch these unusual animals as they feed, swim, and hide among the water plants.

Crayfish are related to crabs and lobsters, and can be found under stones in the shallow water of quiet streams. They do well in aquariums that have stones for them to hide under.

Snails sometimes lay their eggs on the glass sides of aquariums. Then you can watch young snails develop from the eggs.

Tadpoles—also called pollywogs—are young frogs and toads that live in shallow water along the edges of ponds. If tadpoles are well-fed, they gradually turn into adult frogs and toads.

Salamanders are active animals that do well in aquariums. One type—the spotted newt—is common as an adult in fresh-water ponds. However, newts do not mix well with fish.

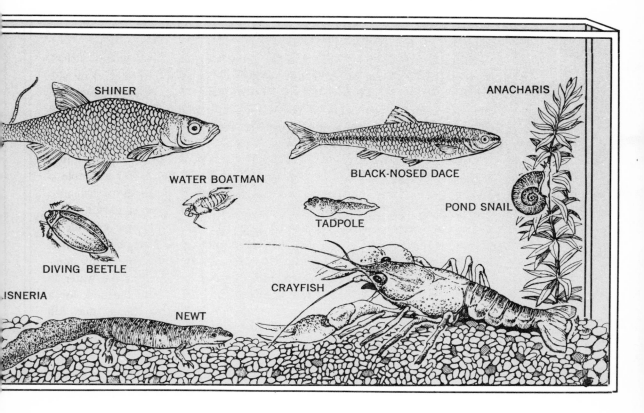

SHINER
ANACHARIS
WATER BOATMAN
BLACK-NOSED DACE
POND SNAIL
TADPOLE
DIVING BEETLE
CRAYFISH
.ISNERIA
NEWT

replace the water that evaporates into the air as water vapor. Be sure that the new water is free of chemicals and is the same temperature as the aquarium water.

The "meat-eating" animals—some fishes, some insects, crayfish, and newts —can be fed bits of lean ground beef, chopped earthworms, small live insects, and prepared fish food. Snails should be fed bits of lettuce, to keep them from eating the aquarium plants. Tadpoles will eat lettuce, spinach, and meaty foods.

The animals should be fed lightly and only once or twice a day. You can skip a day or two without harm. Never give the animals more than they can eat in about five to ten minutes. Leftovers which collect on the bottom should be taken out of the tank every day or so. Aquarium shops sell gadgets that help remove food wastes easily.

How Many Animals?

Water animals can live without plants in an aquarium. Oxygen that the animals need enters the water from the air, and waste carbon dioxide goes into the air from the water.

To find out how many animals your aquarium can support, first measure the length and width of your tank. Then multiply the two measurements to find the number of square inches of water surface. Some aquarium keepers use the rule "an inch of fish for every 4 to 5 square inches of water surface." The surface area is important because this is where the gases enter and leave the water. Divide 4 or 5 into the square inches of your tank surface, and you will find the number of "animal inches" that your tank will probably support.

Keep this rule in mind when you put animals in the water, and then watch to see if the animals seem healthy. If fish come to the surface and gasp, there probably is not enough oxygen for them. The quickest temporary remedy is to dip out some of the water and replace it with fresh water. Then you should remove some animals so there is enough oxygen for all ■

—Nature and Science

16

INVESTIGATIONS

A. After your aquarium animals have been living together for some time, notice if any one animal seems to "boss," or dominate, the other animals. If so, put this animal in another container for a few days. Then put it back in the aquarium. What happens? Is the animal still "boss?" If you add a new animal to the aquarium, watch how the other animals act toward the newcomer. Do they attack it? Do they ignore it? Do they seem to be afraid of it?

B. Minnows have been trained to jump out of the water and grab a bit of food when a red light flashes. You can try to train, or "condition," some of your animals to come to a certain corner of the tank when you blow a whistle. Here is how to do it:

1. Give one fairly loud whistle (about two seconds long) just before you feed the animals. Be sure to give the same signal each time. Whistle before the animals can see you approaching the tank, or they may become trained to the sight of you, and not to your whistle "food signal." The animals will learn faster if you whistle the same way each time.

2. Always feed them at the same corner of the tank, so that they must come to that spot for food.

3. Don't overfeed the animals. (They will learn faster if they are kept slightly hungry.)

4. To speed the animals' training, never give the signal without feeding them, and never feed them without giving the signal.

Before long, the fish (and perhaps some other animals) will begin to learn that your whistle means "food." They will swim to the feeding corner when they hear the signal.

When they have learned this lesson, you can try to teach them to do other things. You might try to teach them to move to different corners when you ring a bell, or flash a light. Keep a record of your investigations and see how long it takes to train your animals. Do some learn faster than others?

Exploring the Lives of Water Snails

■One of the most fascinating kinds of animals that live in ponds can also live in your home. Snails are common animals in fresh-water ponds, and you can collect some by looking for them on the leaves and stems of water plants. Or you can buy some snails from an aquarium supply store. Then you can watch them grow, mate, lay eggs, and raise their young.

Some snails are useful animals to have in aquariums because they eat the simple green plants, called *algae,* that grow on the sides of aquariums. Other snails are a problem because they eat the larger green plants that give an aquarium a natural look.

People who keep fishes in aquariums hunted for a long time to find a snail that would eat algae and left-over food, but would not eat other plants. They tested four kinds (species) of snails called *Ampullaria*. Three of them are terrific plant eaters. The last kind eats only dead leaves, algae, and left-over fish foods. Its full name is *Ampullaria cuprina.* You will find these snails for sale in stores where tropical fish are sold. They cost a few cents, for small ones, to a quarter or more for large ones.

A Home for Snails

Whether you buy or catch your snails, first you must get a home ready. You can keep them in large, wide-mouth jars or in aquariums. A five-gallon aquarium is a practical size. It should be planted with some living plants put in washed sand or fine gravel. The best plants for your snail's home are

18

LARGE WHEEL SNAIL

GREAT POND SNAIL

TADPOLE SNAIL

Vallisneria and *Sagittaria*. You can also try plants collected from a pond.

Put in not less than a dozen *Vallisneria* and one or two *Sagittaria* plants for a five-gallon tank. Double this number for a ten-gallon tank. To keep the plants healthy and growing they must have some kind of food, and the best way to get it is from fish body wastes (droppings). Put three or four *Zebra danios* in your tank. These fishes are available all year around, every pet store has them, and they cost only a few pennies each. They will not bother the snails as many other fishes do. They are hardy and eat anything, and they live two years or even longer.

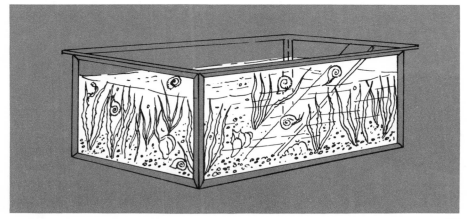

After planting your tank and filling it with cool water from the tap, allow it to stand for two or three days. Put a glass cover on top to keep out dust and cut down evaporation. Then get your fishes and put them in. Float the fish container with the water and fishes in it inside the tank for a couple of hours, to let the water in the container come to the same temperature as the water in the tank. Then gently tip out the fishes.

A day or so after you have put in the fishes you may add two *Ampullaria cuprina* or other snails. Feed the fishes—and the snails too—with the best fish food you can buy. The food should be rich in animal matter—ground shrimp, liver, beef, fish and fish eggs, and a little cereal. You can buy small cans of food like this in pet stores. Do not feed more than will be eaten in about five minutes, then feed again, repeating until the fish leave some of the food. The snails will clean up all the leavings, but do not feed any more for that day or you will foul the water.

Keep your tank where it will get some light for a few hours each day, but not in direct sunlight.

Watching Your Snails

Now start to observe your snails. First of all, see if you can see the motion of a snail's foot muscles. Watch closely as a snail walks up the glass. You will be able to see the rippling movement of the muscles in its foot.

Watch the snails as they walk up leaves, eating the algae that form on the plants. At times the snail will travel to the top without making the leaf move. At other times the leaf will curve downward and gently let the snail drop to the bottom of the tank. Can you figure out why?

Your snails will frequently crawl up to the top of the tank and push their breathing tubes, or *siphons,* up out of the water. They stand with the siphon extended, pumping their bodies just as though they were filling up with air. See if they bend the plant leaves more before they pump themselves up or afterward. Watch the way they let go their hold on the glass and drop to the bottom of the tank. Do they fall faster after pumping up, or slower? Can you figure out why?

After the tank has been set up for a few weeks you may see a green film

This snail was photographed through the glass wall of its aquarium. You can see the tiny teeth on its tongue that are used to scrape algae from the glass.

growing on the glass at the place where the most light hits it. This film is algae, and *Ampullaria cuprina* will eat it. The snail eats by scraping the algae off the glass with its tongue (called a *radula*). The radula is like a ribbon set with rows of tiny teeth. The snail can rotate these teeth to scrape algae from the glass. The teeth of these snails are snowy white, and you can plainly see them and their rotating action.

Notice how fast the algae grow on the glass and how fast the snails eat them. Move the tank closer to or farther away from the light to adjust the rate of growth. If you are careful enough and have patience enough, you can adjust the growth of the algae to match the feeding rate of the snails, and they will keep the tank almost completely clean of algae.

Raising Young Snails

After the snails grow to be about 1½ inches in diameter, they will mate and have young. They lay their eggs out of the water on a surface from which the young snails can drop into the water as they hatch. A good breeding place for your snails is a strip of sanded or ground glass about two inches wide. It should be long enough to stand slanting out of the water in the tank. Some sort of cover should be kept over the tank to keep the air moist above the water, to keep out dust, and to keep the animals from crawling out of the tank.

The strip of ground glass should stick out of the water several inches. It should lean against the side of the tank with its ground surface facing up. The snails will crawl up near the top of the strip and lay their eggs in a large cluster, cementing them firmly to the glass. The eggs are round and pink, and very soft and sticky. After a short time they dry off and the shells harden. In a couple of weeks the eggs hatch and the tiny snails drop into the water.

If you keep the young snails well fed and warm (about 75° F.) they will be ready to breed about eight months after hatching. If you get a large surplus of healthy snails you can trade them with your friends, or sell or trade them to a pet shop owner ■

—Paul Villiard

Dozens of pink eggs are laid out of the water by the female snail. The young drop into the water as they hatch.

Make Your Own Sea Aquarium

■ How would you like to see a live barnacle catching food with its feet? Or a sea urchin gliding on its "tube-feet"?

The best place to see these things is in a salt water aquarium. Not a big public aquarium, but a 10- or 15-gallon aquarium that you can keep right in your own home or school. It can cost you as little as $15 to set up such a miniature ocean (even less if you already have a tank).

The most satisfactory salt water aquariums are all plastic or all glass. Salt water not only rusts the stainless steel of ordinary metal-braced tanks, but may "eat away" the aquarium cement. However, metal-braced tanks have been successfully converted to salt water tanks. You can buy an epoxy sealer (such as Silastic) from aquarium supply shops that covers and protects exposed seams and metal parts.

If you live near the ocean you can probably get some natural sea water. Farther inland, you can buy aquarium salts from an aquarium supply store to make artificial sea water. These aquarium salts will have complete directions on the package. Because ocean water is such a complex substance, it is not practical to try to make up your own combination of chemicals (although this could be an interesting experiment).

Getting Your Ocean Animals

Collecting your own specimens can be fun, and is less expensive than buying them. If you don't live near an ocean, however, write to some of the

22

companies listed in Appendix B for their lists of available salt water animals. A growing number of companies send ocean animals to people who keep salt water aquariums far from an ocean. Whether you collect your own specimens or buy them, you should first have your aquarium tank ready for the animals.

If you can do your own collecting, a rocky beach at low tide is best. You will need clean plastic pails or enamel pails, a net, and a small plastic container. Remember that sea water will react or combine with other substances, especially metals. Just a trace of some metals can make the water poisonous to many small sea animals, so never use metal containers such as galvanized pails or tin cans.

The most difficult part of collecting is getting the specimens from the ocean to the tank, so take only very small animals and lots of water. It is easy to overcrowd the pail. You will probably see so many interesting things that it will be hard to keep from taking too many.

Here is an example of a collection in a 10-quart pail that could be expected to come through a trip of four or five hours in excellent shape: three one-inch hermit crabs, several small prawns, a three-inch starfish, six or seven mud snails, and a very small green crab. Of course you may find entirely different animals when you go collecting—you might discover a little rock entirely covered with barnacles, or you might find feather worms, sea anemones, or a young horseshoe crab.

Very small fish of many species do well in aquariums. Toadfish, killiefish, stickleback, and opaleye (on the west coast) are especially hardy. Many of these fishes are aggressive and may eat smaller specimens. Some of the crabs give the same problem. When you are collecting, do not put a big fish or crab in the same pail with small ones. A big handful of clean seaweed added to the pail gives the small animals some hiding places. Then they will be less likely to try to jump out. To keep the water from sloshing about on the way home, you can stuff some crumpled newspaper into the top of the pail. Another good method of carrying water is to use large extra-heavy plastic bags put inside sturdy cardboard cartons. Be sure the water does not get too warm. A sudden rise in temperature will kill many animals.

Keep Them Alive

Once you have your animals at home, put them into the aquarium right away. Put the animals in gradually, mixing the water in the animal's container with the water in the aquarium, so there is no sudden change in temperature.

Now comes the challenge. Can you keep this collection in a healthy, natural state? Will the aquarium look as attractive a month from now? Will the water stay clear?

If you have kept aquariums before, you already know many of the common pitfalls. A salt water aquarium requires much the same care as an

24

e a few kinds of ocean animals that
ght keep in your aquarium. Photo 1
a hermit crab (left) and a hard-shell
quahog (right). In Photo 2, another
crab is shown in its "home"—an
moon shell. Young hermit crabs live
shells, such as those of periwinkles.
bs move to bigger shells as they
he sea urchin in Photo 3 is eating
om the rock on which it clings with
e feet." Sea urchins are related to
and sand dollars.

ordinary aquarium—plus a few extra precautions.

The first problem is the tank's location. This is important for any aquarium. Too much sunlight will speed the growth of green algae in both fresh and salt water. It is better to depend on an overhead reflector light and keep the aquarium away from direct sunlight. Even in the northern part of the United States, keeping the water cool may be a problem in the summer. During the hottest days ice cubes (kept in a plastic bag) may have to be added occasionally. On the other hand, if you have fish or other animals from tropical waters, summer weather is just right. In this case, when the temperature drops much below 75° F. you will need a heater and thermostat (available from aquarium supply stores).

Most plants from the ocean are difficult to keep healthy. It is best to do without them, at least until you have had more experience in keeping a salt water aquarium. This does not mean that you will have a bare tank. Rocks, coral, and sand can be arranged to make your aquarium look like a bit of ocean floor. But don't use ordinary sand or rocks of mixed minerals; they may contain substances that will poison your animals. If you get seashore sand be sure it is perfectly clean. Rinse it several times in fresh water to remove all impurities.

Any pure quartz rocks are safe, and you can buy pure quartz sand especially for aquariums from aquarium supply shops or dealers. Coral must be thoroughly "cured" before it is safe. Soak the coral a day or two in fresh water, then see whether it has an odor. If it has even the slightest odor it may poison your ocean animals and must be soaked again until the odor disappears.

How To Keep an Ocean

If you have only a few small specimens (for example, two periwinkles, a one-inch hermit crab, and a two-inch baby flounder), it is possible to keep them in a five-gallon aquarium without any filter. It is safer to use a filter, however, and if you get more animals, a filter will be necessary. Use a 10- or 15-gallon tank if you can. It is easier to keep the temperature constant in a big tank.

You will need to buy a pump and filter from a pet store or aquarium dealer. They cost about $6. (A larger tank with many occupants may re-

1.025

When a hydrometer is put into ocean water, it usually floats at the 1.025 mark. If the water gets more salty, the hydrometer floats higher—a reminder to add some fresh water.

quire more than one filter and a stronger pump.)

Your tank should be covered with a sheet of glass to keep water from escaping into the air (*evaporating*). Add fresh water from time to time to make up for the water that does evaporate. When you first fill the tank it is a good idea to mark the water line. Then always be sure that the water is at that level. When you add water, use tap water that has stood for a day or so to let the chlorine evaporate.

To check the amount of salt in the water, use a glass float called a *hydrometer*. Notice the markings on the side of the hydrometer. When you first put the hydrometer into the salt water, it will probably float at the 1.025 to 1.030 mark. Later, if the hydrometer rises above this line, add the tap water to make it less salty. If you have added too much fresh water, the hydrometer will sink below the 1.025 mark. In general, you will find that most shore animals will stand water fresher than normal better than water that is too salty.

Even when you use a filter, your salt water aquarium will need some cleaning. To keep algae from growing, you should wipe the inside surface of the glass with a clean rag or glass wool (and be sure your hands are clean).

Take out the top layer of sand once in a while, rinse it with fresh water, and return it to the tank. This is best done with a section of plastic tubing about a half inch in diameter and about four feet long. Use it as a siphon. First fill the tubing with water by holding both ends under the faucet, then

To keep your aquarium clean, use plastic tubing to siphon the top layer of sand from the tank into a pail. Then return the sand to the tank after rinsing it with fresh water.

hold the ends shut with your thumbs. Put one end into the tank where the sand is to be removed and the other end into a pail placed below the bottom level of the tank. You can control the removal of dirty sand by keeping your thumb at the tube end in the pail, ready to shut off the flow. Control the pick-up end in the tank with your other hand. If you have enough bottom-feeding animals and sand-burrowing animals, this chore need not be done very often.

Feeding and Watching

You will need at least 10 or 15 minutes daily to prepare food and give it to your animals. Then, an hour or two later, you will need another five minutes to remove any uneaten food—to prevent pollution.

Some of the animals you may have, such as nudibranchs, periwinkles, and sea urchins, are algae eaters. Most of the other sea animals you'll have are likely to be meat-eaters. Many of them will eat tiny bits of chopped clam, shrimp, or fish. Very small earthworms (or cut up pieces) make good food. Others will want live food. You can often buy live tubifex worms, daphnia, blood worms, and adult brine shrimp from aquarium supply stores. Barnacles and small sea anemones will eat newly-hatched brine shrimp. You can buy the brine shrimp eggs and hatch them yourself (*see "Raise Your Own Brine Shrimp," on page 95*). You may have to do some experimenting before you find the food that best suits your animals. That is why you should take your time, sit down, and watch what happens after you put the food into the water. You may find that one large crab is eating everything in sight!

It is wise to take a few minutes each day to watch your aquarium for another reason. You should become familiar with the normal actions of each animal in the tank. If an animal shows signs of distress, put it in a separate container. Watch closely because some ocean animals move very little, and any dead animal can pollute the water.

If, despite your best efforts, you wake up some morning and find the water cloudy, don't despair. First, try to find the source of pollution and remove it. Then use extra filters (it's good to have one or two extras for just such emergencies). If you have extra salt water, now is the time to use it. Usually, by replacing one third of the water and adding extra filters, you can clear up murky water in two or three days with little or no loss of life. (Any salt water you remove can be kept in a glass container in a dark place for a few weeks. It will clear up and can be used again.)

There is much to be learned about many kinds of salt water animals. Try keeping careful records on some of yours. For example: How do they eat their food? How much do they eat? Do they shed their skins? If so, how often? How long do they live? How do they act toward other animals? You may discover some information that will help others who keep salt water aquariums ■

—*Barbara Neill*

28

How to Keep and Study Young Turtles

■ Young turtles are harmless, fascinating animals that you can easily care for and study. You can buy them from pet shops or variety stores. Most young turtles sold as pets are either red-eared turtles or Mississippi map turtles, but they may be any of a dozen or more kinds. The proprietor of a pet shop may be able to help you identify yours.

A small aquarium is an ideal turtle home, and a five-gallon aquarium is big enough for about a half dozen young turtles. Although many turtles spend most of their lives in water, they need to climb out onto dry land once in a while. One way to give your turtles both land and water is to put rocks or pieces of wood into the aquarium. Make sure that the rocks are close-grained, without sharp edges that will cause sores on the turtles' lower shells. You can also make a sloping beach of sand for the turtles to crawl onto, but sand is hard to keep clean.

Turtles often sun themselves. However, window ledges are often drafty in winter and very hot in summer. For a "sun," set a gooseneck lamp near the aquarium. This will also help warm the water. If the water temperature goes below 70 degrees Fahrenheit, turtles are likely to become sluggish and refuse to eat. A temperature of from 75 to 80 degrees is ideal for most kinds of turtles.

Most of the millions of young turtles sold each year die from neglect, and the most common cause of death is starvation. Be sure to feed your turtles well. They should be fed three or four times a week, with fresh raw hamburger, raw chopped fish, or chopped earthworms. Most turtles eat some plants, so fruits and lettuce should be fed to them occasionally. A little powdered calcium (from a drug store) should be mixed with their food once in a while. It helps the growth of the turtles' bones and shells.

Raw meat can make a mess in an aquarium, so remove any uneaten food after letting the turtles feed for about an hour. Whenever the water gets dirty, replace it with clean water of about the same temperature. Incidentally, many turtles can eat only underwater, so there should be at least an inch of water in the aquarium.

The best way to tell whether a young turtle is receiving a good diet is to observe its growth. Weigh and measure it every two weeks or so. A healthy, well-fed turtle may double its size in a year. A turtle that does not grow at all is really slowly starving to death.

Most kinds of young turtles sold as pets live in shallow, marshy places in the wild, and these kinds do well when kept under the conditions just described. However, there are two other groups of turtles that are some-times sold, and these groups do not live the way the more common kinds of pet turtles do. *Tortoises* are turtles that live on land, usually in very dry places. They are quite easy to identify, because they have high, curved shells. If tortoises are kept in water, they will soon die. In fact, tortoises are quite difficult to keep healthy, and you should not buy one unless you have had experience with keeping the more common turtles.

The other group of turtles sometimes sold as pets live in deep water in the wild. Young snapping turtles and musk turtles are members of this group that are often seen in pet shops. While the deep-water turtles will live in shallow water, they should be kept in an aquarium with water at least six inches deep. The deep-water turtles do not need anything to climb out of the water on, but they should have rocks on the bottom to use as hiding places.

Studying Your Turtles

Once your turtles are established in an aquarium, you can begin to study them. For example, how does a turtle swim? Does it use its tail? How are

RED-EARED TURTLE

FLORIDA COOTER TURTLE

PAINTED TURTLE

MISSISSIPPI MAP TURTLE

its feet used? Can a turtle swim backward?

Here are some other ways that you can investigate the lives of turtles:

1. Turtles are cold-blooded animals, which means that their body temperature is near the temperature of their surroundings. You can use a thermometer and some ice cubes to observe the effect of cold temperatures on turtles.

Put a turtle into a jar or other container with water that is fairly warm— about 75 to 80 degrees Fahrenheit. The water should be deep enough for the turtle to put its nose above the surface while standing on the bottom. Measure the temperature of the water with the thermometer. Then count the number of times that the turtle comes to the surface for air in a half-hour. Keep notes of your findings.

Add several ice cubes and wait until the temperature goes down to about 50 degrees. Count the number of times the turtle comes to the surface for air at this new temperature. Does the turtle breathe faster or slower at the low temperature? In what other ways does the cold water affect the turtle's behavior?

2. If you have several turtles of the same kind, you can compare their growth while feeding them different foods. First, divide your turtles into two groups. To tell them apart, put a dot of enamel paint on the upper shell, or *carapace,* of the turtles in one group. Leave the other turtles unmarked.

Feed the turtles in two different feeding pans. One group should be fed hamburger, lettuce, and fruit. Feed the other group "turtle food" which you can buy from a pet shop or variety store. Weigh the turtles every two or three weeks and find the average weight of each group. Keep a record of your findings. Which group grows the fastest? Which food is better for your turtles?

3. Does color influence the turtles' choice of food? Try offering your turtles chopped raw fish colored with vegetable dye. Do they prefer certain colors? ■

—*Alan Mark Fletcher*

Keep your turtles in an aquarium that has at least an inch of water in it. Turtles must have some smooth stones to climb onto, and you may have to set a lamp nearby to keep the water temperature near 75 degrees F.

The Ways
of Fishes

The Guppy's Secret Life

■ People first began to keep guppies as pets in 1908, and scientists have studied them for many years. Most of that time these bold, active fish have led a secret life, right under the noses of the people who were watching and breeding them. Everyone knew that guppies are born live, instead of hatching from eggs as many fish do. But no one understood their ways of reproduction. Scientists know better now, but they still have a lot to learn about the guppy.

Except for the goldfish, the guppy has for years been the most popular of all aquarium pets. It is small and hardy, and it lives well in small aquariums. Scientists use it as a sort of aquatic "guinea pig." With simple care, you too can keep guppies and investigate their lives.

Some Rules for Keeping Guppies

The water in which fish live is very much a part of their lives, and the slightest pollution can kill them. Like all fishes, guppies are sensitive to metals (especially copper, silver, zinc, and chromium). Such things as disinfectants, soaps, detergents, insecticides, chlorine, tobacco, paint, and many plastics may also kill them. Try to keep everything out of the aquarium except what is definitely known to be safe. A cover of glass kept on top will help. The aquarium should be made so that only glass touches the water inside it.

Sudden changes of any kind are bad for fish, and sudden changes in temperature are often fatal. If the temperature in the room gets below

33

72° F., your aquarium will have to have a water heater and thermostat.

Water that comes from the faucet is perfectly suitable for people to drink, but the chlorine and metal in it may poison fish. To use such water in an aquarium, first leave it in an open glass container for several days. This allows the chlorine to escape into the air and improves the water greatly for fish life, especially if some aquatic plants are put into the water. This is called "conditioning."

Fish like the guppy will "condition" their own water, too, because, up to a point, their waste products will improve their environment. But too much of this waste matter will interfere with the growth and reproduction of aquarium fishes. So, every two to three weeks you should replace about one quarter of the water with fresh, clean water—conditioned, if possible.

Don't leave leftover food or dead fish in the water for long; they will decay and give off substances that are very poisonous. Your aquarium

This high-speed photo shows a male guppy (right) trying to mate with the larger female. The small white arrow points to the male's gonopodium, which has swung forward. Most attempts to mate are unsuccessful. Only when the fish are joined together for a few seconds is mating successful.

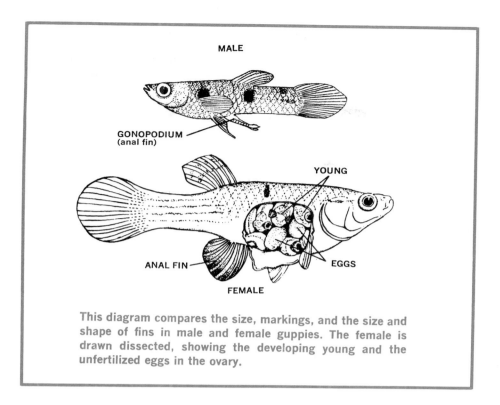

MALE

GONOPODIUM
(anal fin)

YOUNG

ANAL FIN

EGGS

FEMALE

This diagram compares the size, markings, and the size and shape of fins in male and female guppies. The female is drawn dissected, showing the developing young and the unfertilized eggs in the ovary.

should be kept clean at all times. "Vacuum cleaning" it with a siphon is the easiest way (*see page 27*). If you siphon the water into a *clean glass* container, some of it may be siphoned back after the dirt has been allowed to settle out of it.

Feeding Your Guppies

Like your four-footed pets, guppies will learn to "beg" for food and sometimes act as if they are hungry even when they are not. The only way to know that fish have had enough to eat, but not too much, is to watch them carefully, making sure that they eat up every little bit that they are fed. After a while, you will learn just how much your fish will eat, and you won't have to watch every mouthful or clean up after meals.

Feed your guppies each morning to keep them breeding regularly. (Three feedings a day are not too much for young fish, but be extra careful not to overfeed them.) Use different kinds of food, both the dry and the wet (paste) kinds that are sold in pet stores. Also try some live food, such as daphnia, brine shrimp, white worms, or tubifex worms. If you can't get any live food from a pet shop, some frozen brine shrimp or daphnia may be used.

Many people believe that plants are needed in an aquarium to supply oxygen, but plants add oxygen to the water only when they are in bright light. Unless an aquarium has too many fish in it, all the oxygen that is needed will pass into the water from the air above.

A pair of guppies can live very well in a one-gallon container, but you

35

should remove their offspring as soon as they start to grow. This will prevent overcrowding.

Guppy Courting and Mating

There is always a lot going on in a tankful of guppies. In fact, there is so much activity that it is difficult to study what any particular fish is doing. If you want to see how male guppies court females and mate with them, first put a male into a one- or two-gallon container. After about an hour, the female may be added. Unless the male feels "at home," he will pay little or no attention to the other fish.

You will see a great deal of courtship activity—the male will swim around the female and turn its body into an S shape. You should not be surprised if you don't see any mating for some time.

How Guppies Are Born

In the mating process, the male deposits its sex cells, called *sperms,* inside the body of the female. The sperms can live there, in the female's *ovary,* for at least eight months, fertilizing batches of eggs as they become ripe. In this way, the sperms from one mating can produce as many as eight broods of guppies—one brood every 21 to 28 or more days, depending on the amount of light and the temperature in the aquarium. Once the eggs have been fertilized, the young guppies will develop in about 20 days.

Few people have ever seen a female guppy give birth to her brood. The young fish are usually born head first. It takes a minute or so for each one to come out, and two or three may appear one right after another. A female may bear 70 or 80 young within three to four hours.

One of the first things a newborn guppy must do is swim to the surface and gulp a bubble of air to fill its *gas bladder.* (This bladder is a sac inside the fish's body that helps reduce its weight and allows the fish to swim without great effort.) Until this happens, the tiny fish may be easy prey for an adult guppy, even its own mother. Some floating plants in your aquarium will provide hiding places near the surface for the young guppies ∎

—James W. Atz

36

The Bubble Nests of Betta splendens

■Have you ever heard of a fish that makes its nest of bubbles? Or a male fish that chases the females away after she lays her eggs, and brings up the young fish himself? This remarkable fish is known as Betta, or the Siamese fighting fish called *Betta splendens*. It is the tamest kind of fish I know of and is easy to take care of in a home aquarium. Also, unlike many other animals, Bettas do not seem shy in captivity. They breed and carry out their daily lives even though you are watching them.

Bettas have been bred for fighting in Siam for hundreds of years. They have long flowing fins and come in a number of strikingly lovely colors. Unlike most fishes, they breathe air, gulping mouthfuls at the surface of the water. Because of this habit they can be kept in unusually small bowls. Some people raise the young fish in pint jars. One of the most popular aquarium fishes, Bettas can be bought at many pet stores.

Building a Bubble Nest

Your Betta will soon get to know you, especially if you feed him at about the same time each day. If you are gentle, he will let you stroke him with your finger, or even allow you to pick him up out of the water briefly in your cupped hand. But be careful. With a quick flick of the tail he may jump out of your hand.

If your male Betta is in good health and is kept warm (80° F.), he will probably build a bubble nest. Using inhaled air, the male forms a slimy

37

bubble in his mouth. Just how he does this is not known. He places bubble after bubble at the water surface in a chosen place. In an aquarium this will often be in one corner or wherever a shadow falls. In nature, the male may use floating plants to anchor the nest.

When it is finished, the nest is about the size and shape of a small scoop of ice cream that has melted until it is about one-half inch high in the center. Because the bubbles keep breaking, the male is kept busy adding new ones.

It is easy to raise Bettas, and it is a fascinating performance to watch. When the female is full of eggs, as shown by her enlarged belly, she should be placed in the same bowl as the male. At first you should keep the two fish apart. If you don't, the male might attack the female and injure her. A piece of glass separating the two fish will protect the female and allow her to adjust to her new surroundings.

When you first bring the two together, the female will flee from the male. This is typical. But you will see that she does not flee too fast. In fact, if you watch closely, you will observe that while swimming away from the male she swims with wider than normal motions, as though she were "swaggering" away from him. Also she may tip down so that her head is lower than her tail. Dark bands may appear on her body.

The male does not attack her. Instead, he responds by swimming around her. His fins are fully spread, making him look larger than he actually is. His colors, too, become darker than before, bringing out their shiny highlights and making him more easily seen. Unlike the female, the male tends to tilt upward, his head slightly higher than his tail.

Finally the female moves toward the male. In response, he swims toward the nest and the female may follow him. Once there, he adds a few bubbles to the nest. All during this time the male seems about to attack the female. Indeed, sometimes he does. But the female presses closer to the male, nudging him in the side with her snout. When this happens, the male folds into a U and wraps himself around the female. He holds her in this position, called the spawning embrace, *fertilizing* the fresh eggs that she lays by adding sperm cells to them. Without the sperm cells, the eggs would not hatch into young fish.

38

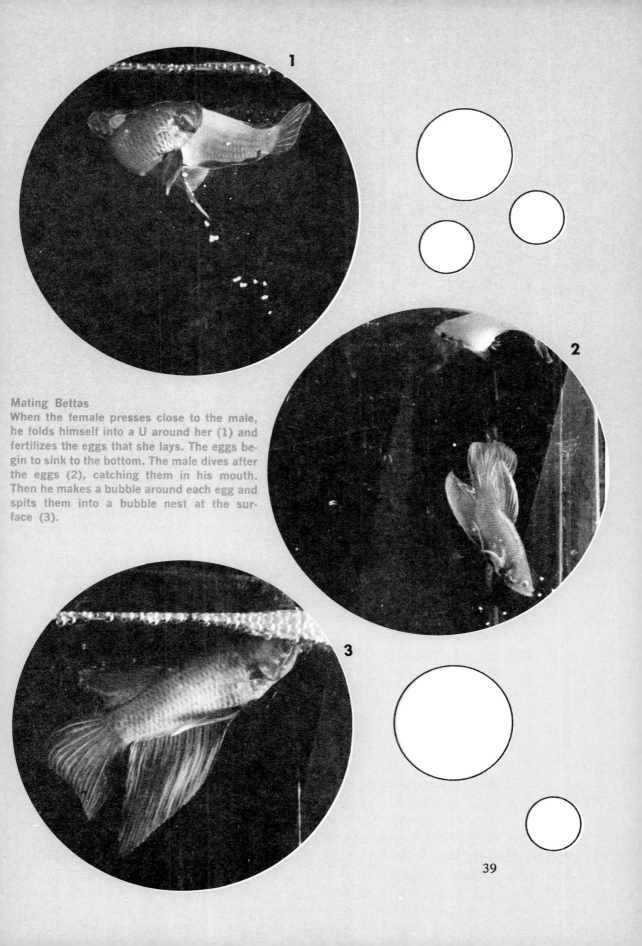

Mating Bettas
When the female presses close to the male, he folds himself into a U around her (1) and fertilizes the eggs that she lays. The eggs begin to sink to the bottom. The male dives after the eggs (2), catching them in his mouth. Then he makes a bubble around each egg and spits them into a bubble nest at the surface (3).

39

Within a few seconds the male lets her go and dives after the sinking eggs, catching them in his mouth. He puts bubbles around each egg and spits them into the bubble nest. Then he returns to the female.

Spawning may go on for an hour or two. In the end the female flees. If she is not removed from the aquarium, the male may kill her.

Guarding the Eggs

The male stays with the eggs and guards them. If other male Bettas are around, he chases them away. If an egg drops out of the bubble nest, the father Betta catches it in his mouth, wraps it in bubbles, and puts it back into the nest.

In about two days, the eggs hatch into tiny new fish, called *larval* fish. These have little "glue spots," or cement glands, on their heads and elsewhere. With the help of the cement glands, the larval fish stick to the leaves of plants.

The father Betta protects his young ones and catches any that come loose and begin to drift away. After two or three more days, the baby fish lose their cement glands and hover in the water at the nest. As they grow, the little fish start to drift away from the nest. When that happens, the male "stirs" the water by quickly beating the large fins just behind the gill openings (*pectoral* fins). This action causes the young fish to swim to him. He takes them into his mouth and spits them out under the nest. Within two days or so, however, the baby fish, often called *fry* at this stage, swim off on their own.

The Mouth-Breeders

A close relative of Betta breeds in a remarkably different way. This fish, *Betta anabatoides,* is sometimes called the "mouth-breeding" Betta. They are hard to find in aquarium shops.

During the spawning embrace, the male manages to end up so that his bottom middle fin (*anal* fin) forms a shallow cup under the female. The eggs are dropped into this cup. The female next picks them up in her mouth after each embrace. Then the two fish face each other. She spits the eggs at the male one by one. He catches them in his mouth and keeps them there. After many embraces, the male swims off with all the eggs in his mouth. For about a week and a half, he keeps them in his mouth where they develop and hatch. He then releases the fry into the water and they swim away. No bubble nest is built.

This method of breeding makes sense when you know how the fish live. The mouth breeder lives in streams. A delicate bubble nest built in a flowing stream probably would be broken up by the current and all the bubbles containing the eggs broken or scattered. The Bettas have no such problems because they live in quiet waters ■

—*George W. Barlow*

40

Battling Bettas

■We can never know if an animal sees the world around it in the same way we do. For instance, we know that a dummy in a store window is not a real person. Yet little girls treat dolls as "babies," even though they know that dolls are not alive.

The Siamese fighting fish you read about in the last chapter will "fight" with a model that you would easily recognize as being a fake fish. Sometimes they fight things that do not even resemble other fish. One male that I kept fought the silvery bulb of the thermometer when I took the water temperature. Yet, in an aquarium, a Betta seldom attempts to fight with any kind of fish except another Betta.

You might ask, then, how does a Betta know which is a Betta, and which is not? One way to answer this is to make models that look something like Bettas and present them to a Betta. The Betta responds to some models more than to others. So you can find out how much the model must look like a real Betta before your fish reacts to it.

One of the important lessons to learn from this is that a Betta may respond to several quite different models in quite different ways. For example, a male might attack a red model without eyes as much as a blue model with eyes. A model combining eyes and red color might cause even more attacking.

Betta Fights Follow a Pattern

Before you make the models you should know how one live Betta responds to another live Betta. If two male Bettas are put into the same tank,

Two male Bettas in a tank challenge each
other to fight by swimming side by side,
their fins spread like sails.

they may start to fight and continue until one is clearly the winner; then they should be separated. Bettas bred especially for fighting may fight for several hours. A Betta not bred for fighting seldom battles more than 15 minutes.

No two Betta fights are ever alike. Yet all of them have some things in common. For one, the fish will nearly always show the same displays—meaning certain acts that occur again and again and are easy to see. Second, the fight takes place in stages.

In most fights there is first a stage when the two males approach one another. As they get near, their colors become vivid, they spread their fins, and their gill covers swing out, revealing bright red borders.

The next stage is often the longest. It could be called the *display period.* The two males spend much of their time swimming in the same direction, side by side, with fins spread like enormous sails. Now they come to the surface for air more often. At this stage it is possible to see that the pelvic fin closest to the other male is held stiffly down. The other pelvic fin is held against the belly, or opened and closed like scissors.

As the two fish swim along, one turns his head, with raised gill covers, and looks at the other, who in turn looks slightly away. Suddenly the one doing the looking straightens his head. The one looking slightly away sees this, and in a moment he turns his head and stares at his opponent. On they swim, trading stares. From time to time one swings his tail in a wide beat, sending water currents to the other, who may also reply with a tail beat. Sometimes they tilt up as they tail beat, even standing straight up on their tails.

The display period is the most important and interesting part of the fight. Each male is testing his opponent. In this way the males make clear who is the stronger. In nature, the fight usually ends here because one male swims away, leaving the stronger male the best place for spawning. That is what the fight is all about.

In an aquarium, neither fish can leave. For this reason a fight between two Bettas should be stopped at this stage. If it is not, real combat will take place. They begin ramming and biting one another. The lovely fins are ripped to shreds in short order.

Finally one male hesitates before ramming the other. Suddenly he stops fighting. He folds his fins, his colors fade, and a dark stripe may appear, running the length of his body. This seems to mean "I give up" and is the last stage of the fight. As long as the loser does not move, he will not be attacked. But the moment he stirs, the winner rushes to bite him. Now the loser must have air but the winner stands over him to keep him from swimming to the surface. If the loser is not removed from the tank at this time, he may die.

When Do Bettas Fight?

It is a mistake to think that a male Betta will always fight another Betta or a model with the same vigor. These fish are not like machines. Bettas learn to know and, for a while, remember each other. If one has recently been defeated by another, the loser will not fight back much if he meets the winner again. If a male has not fought for a long time, he will display to almost anything.

On the other hand, a male who is challenged to fight often is less and less ready to fight. Remember this when you are tempted to hold a mirror up to

INVESTIGATION

How to Test a Betta's Fight Response

Models of Bettas are easy to make. Because they will not be put into the water, you can make them of thin cardboard or stiff paper.

Draw an outline of the fish with the fins spread, the same size as your Betta, then cut it out with scissors. A piece of styrofoam, or clay, can also be worked into the shape of a Betta. Try paper of various colors, or paint your cut-out. Details such as eyes and mouth can be put in with a fine brush, using black and white paint.

Now take a piece of stiff wire about one foot long. Bend it sharply at one end to make a handle. Run the other end into the belly of your model, or tape it in that position.

Trying Out Your Model

To test your Betta, hold the end of the wire so that your hand is hidden behind, say, the edge of a table. Hold the model against the glass wall of your Betta's bowl or aquarium. Watch how your fish responds. After one-half minute, quickly remove the model. That is the *stationary* test. In the *moving* test, make the model slowly "swim" the length of the glass, turn, and swim back. Do this for one-half minute.

To decide how well your Betta responds, you must score his behavior. Give a number to each of his actions and write it down each time that action occurs. Here is a simple system: approach=1, spread fins=2, raised gill covers =3, tail beat=4, ram=5. Your record might be 1, 2, 3, 4, 3, 4, 3, 5— which adds up to 25 for a total response.

There are several things about Bettas that you can inquire into. Color for one. The original Bettas are thought to have been red. Does a red model cause more responses than a blue, green, or yellow model? And what about markings? Try adding to your model, and removing from it the eyes, mouth, red border on the gill covers, and the long body stripe. Or add and remove fins. Turn the model upside down or move it backward. Give it two heads instead of a head and a tail.

You can also do much with a mirror by covering most of it with tape. How small a piece of his own image will your Betta respond to?

A final word of caution. Bettas learn that the models can be ignored, so do not test your male too often, or too many times in a row.

your Betta. If you do it too often, the Betta may stop reacting to his reflection. Fighting also depends on water temperature, hunger, and health. A male with eggs in a bubble nest is more ready to fight than one without a nest. And just as with people, there are individual differences. Some Bettas are more apt to fight than others ■

—*George W. Barlow*

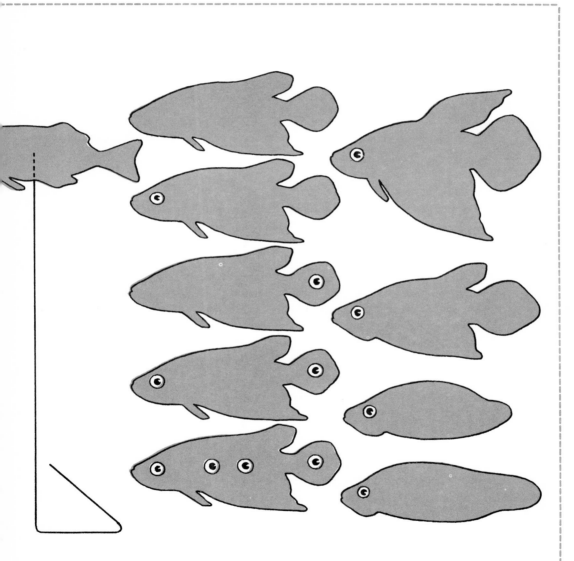

Run a piece of stiff wire into the model fish's belly so you can move it from below the aquarium. Try painting eyes on the model in different places, as shown, and see how your Betta reacts to each. Another way to test your Betta is to change the size and number of fins on the model, as shown here.

Gulp . . . Gulp . . . Gulp . . . Goes the Goldfish

■ Watch a fish continually gulping water as it swims around, and you might think it should drown. But "drowning" means not being able to get oxygen because your lungs are full of water, or some other liquid. Without lungs, a fish can't drown. Do you think it can suffocate for lack of oxygen?

The water that a fish gulps in passes over, under, and around its *gills*— tiny *filaments,* or folds of thin skin, under the flaps just behind the fish's head. Oxygen that is dissolved in the water passes through the walls of these filaments into the fish's blood stream, just as oxygen from the air passes through the thin walls of tiny tubes that carry blood through your lungs.

The oxygen is combined with hydrogen in the fish's body cells to form water. This is part of a complicated process in which energy and carbon dioxide are released from food in the cells. The carbon dioxide, a waste, is carried in the blood stream back to the gills. There it passes back into the water and out the fish's *gill slits,* while the flaps are open.

The process of taking in oxygen (from the atmosphere or from water) and expelling waste carbon dioxide is called *respiration.* You can get an idea of how much oxygen an animal is using by the number of respirations it makes in one minute. (Each time a fish opens and closes its gill flaps it is taking one "breath.")

How Does Activity Affect a Fish's "Breathing"?

Do you think that a fish uses more oxygen when it is active than when it is resting? Does the temperature of the water have any effect on a fish's respiration? Here are some ways to find out.

You will need four goldfish. Comet goldfish can withstand temperature changes better than other kinds, and it is easy to see their gill flaps opening. You can buy them at a tropical fish store for 20 to 50 cents each. You will also need three containers. Flat-sided tanks are better than round bowls, which make the fish appear distorted. You might use clear plastic sweater boxes from a variety store, but only for your investigations. (The plastic may have a bad effect on the fish over a long period of time.) And you will need a thermometer to check the temperature of the water in your tanks.

Place the fish in a tank with water at 70° F. (You can regulate the temperature by stirring in warmer or cooler water as needed—but do that *before* you put the fish in the tank.) Move one fish to another tank with water at 70°. Darken the room for a few minutes, then turn on the lights from a distance and approach the test tank slowly. The fish should be fairly quiet. Count the number of times its gill flaps open and close in one minute. Do this several times and find the average. Record this figure in a table like Table 1 on the next page.

When the fish is moving a bit faster, take several more counts. Then stir water just enough to excite the fish, and count its respirations when it is swimming rapidly. Do the same thing with each fish, putting each one into the third tank (also at 70°) when you are through testing it.

Temperature and Respiration

Be sure to check the temperature of the water *each time* you count respirations. If the temperature has changed more than one or two degrees, record it with your respiration count. Fish are coldblooded animals, so their temperature changes with the temperature of their surroundings. Do you think that a change in water temperature will affect the respiration of a fish a great deal?

To find out, fill two tanks with water at 70°, and put two fish into each of them. Count their respirations separately, and record them in Table 2. Then stir a little warm water into one tank to heat up the water in the tank evenly, and bring it up to 75°. Add the warm water *very slowly* so that you won't shock the fish. Take at least 15 minutes to a half hour to raise the water temperature five degrees. Count the respirations of the fish in the "warm" tank again, and write the numbers down. Then raise the temperature of the water another five degrees, to 80°, and record the respirations. Watch to see if the fish begin swimming to the surface as the water gets warmer (can you guess why?). If this happens, don't add any more warm water.

Now stir cold water into the other tank *very slowly*. Take 15 minutes to a

COMET GOLDFISH

1 Fish Respirations per Minute at 70°F

activity of fish	fish 1	fish 2	fish 3	fish 4
resting				
normal				
active				

2 Fish Respirations per Minute at Varying Temperatures
(Normal Activity)

water tempera-ture	warming water		cooling water	
	fish 1	fish 2	fish 3	fish 4
80°F				
75°				
70°				
65°				
60°				
55°				

half hour to lower the temperature five degrees. Count and record the respirations of the two fish at 65°, and at each 5-degree step down to 55°.

What Did You Find Out?

From the findings in your two tables, how would you describe the effect of activity on a fish's respiration? How does heat or cold affect its respiration? Does the size of the fish seem to make any difference in the way activity or heat affects its respiration? Can you think of some possible explanations for your findings? ■ 　　　　　　　　　　　　　　　　　　　　*—Anthony Joseph*

INVESTIGATIONS

Do you think that vibrations outside the tank will speed up or slow down a fish's respiration? (Try placing the tank near a loudspeaker.) What if you dissolve some salt in the water (no more than a teaspoonful per gallon)? Does the strength of the light in the tank have any effect? How about the color of the light? You can probably think of many other ways to investigate things that change the speed of a fish's respiration.

Exploring the Micro-World

■ Until about 300 years ago, no man had seen a living creature smaller than a cheese mite, a spider-like animal about the size of the dot on this i. But then a Dutch cloth merchant, a man of great curiosity, discovered hundreds of far smaller plants and animals with a simple one-lens microscope.

Anton van Leeuwenhoek's simple instrument and his drawings of what he had seen astonished the most learned men of his day. Today we have the advantage of far better microscopes and all the knowledge that scientists have gained since the time of Leeuwenhoek. With a microscope, you too can explore the "invisible world" with the same excitement as Leeuwenhoek.

Through a simple magnifying glass, you can see an object as if it were three to 12 times as large as it actually is, depending on the magnifying power of the lens. A "portable microscope"—a tube that looks like a fountain pen and has a lens in each end—will enlarge an object up to 40 or 50 times. But you have to hold either of these instruments at just the right distance from an object in order to see it clearly, or *in focus*.

A regular microscope also has a tube with two or more magnifying lenses mounted in it. The tube is held in a stand that also has a table, or *stage,* to hold the object you are looking at. There is a hole in the stage, with a mirror under it to reflect light up through the object. By turning a knob, you can move the tube up or down to bring the object into focus.

The lens you look through is called the *eyepiece lens,* and the one closest to the object is the *objective lens.* The magnifying power of each of these lenses is usually marked on the tube ("10X" means that the lens en-

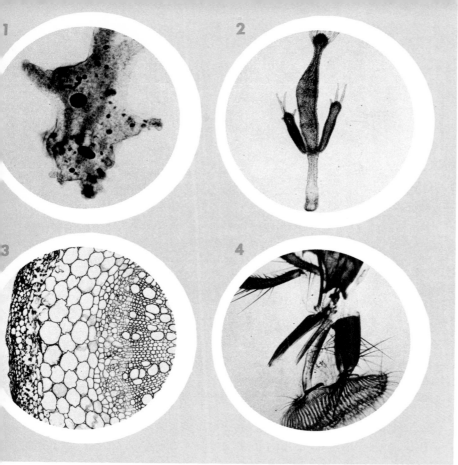

These are some of the fascinating things that you can see with a microscope that magnifies 50 to 200 times: (1) Amoeba proteus, a shapeless, one-celled animal; (2) Hydra, a larger, many-celled animal; (3) cells in a potato stem; (4) the large pad-shaped tongue of a fly (bottom of photo).

larges an object 10 times). You can find the total magnifying power of your microscope by multiplying the magnifying power of the eyepiece lens, say 10X, by that of the objective lens, say 20X. In this case, the microscope magnifies the object 10 times 20, or 200 times. Some microscopes have several different objective lenses so that you can enlarge an object by different amounts.

Operating Your Microscope

To use a microscope, you will need some slides, cover glasses, Canada balsam, tweezers, an eyedropper, and a collecting bottle. You can buy these at little cost from a drugstore, or from a biological supply house.

A good kind of specimen to look at first through your microscope is something flat, like a human hair. Put it on a glass slide and lay a cover glass on top. Place the slide on the microscope stage with the specimen under the objective lens. If your microscope has more than one objective lens, start with the lens of the lowest magnifying power. Now you are ready to make some adjustments.

LIGHT. Place your lamp several inches away from the mirror and tilt the mirror at an angle of about 45 degrees. Look through the eyepiece lens. Adjust the mirror until you get bright, even lighting. Move the lamp nearer or farther away if necessary. If you don't have a microscope lamp, try a table lamp at a distance of a foot or two.

51

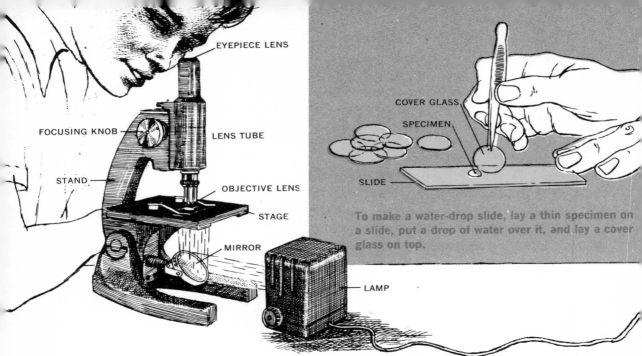

Figure labels (left illustration): EYEPIECE LENS, FOCUSING KNOB, LENS TUBE, STAND, OBJECTIVE LENS, STAGE, MIRROR, LAMP

Figure labels (right illustration): COVER GLASS, SPECIMEN, SLIDE

To make a water-drop slide, lay a thin specimen on a slide, put a drop of water over it, and lay a cover glass on top.

You can also light specimens from above the stage if your lamp is bright enough. For best results, put a piece of black construction paper under the slide. This kind of lighting is especially good for seeing animals in pond water.

FOCUSING. Some microscopes have only one knob for focusing the lenses. But if your microscope has two knobs, one is for making rough adjustments and the other for fine adjustments. The rough-focus knob moves the tube fast, and the fine-focus knob moves it slowly.

Before putting your eye to the eyepiece lens, move the tube down to about an eighth of an inch above the slide. Then look through the eyepiece lens and move the tube *upward* to bring the image into focus. Focusing upward when your eye is at the lens keeps you from jamming the objective lens down into the slide.

Learn to keep both eyes open. If you have trouble doing this, cut a hole in a piece of black construction paper and mount it on the microscope tube. Then your free eye is concentrated on the black paper.

Usually you won't be able to see all parts of a specimen clearly at one time. By carefully turning the fine-focus knob, you can bring different levels of the specimen into focus. Thick specimens usually should be cut into thin slices to let light through.

How To Mount Specimens on Slides

A water-drop slide is useful for many specimens you wish to examine. Use an eyedropper to place a drop of water over a thin specimen on a slide, then put a cover glass over the drop.

A small insect can be held on a slide with a piece of clear sticky tape. Clear gelatin can also be used. Put the specimen on a cover glass and put one drop of gelatin-and-water mixture over it and one drop on a slide. Set

52

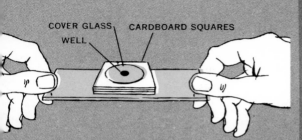

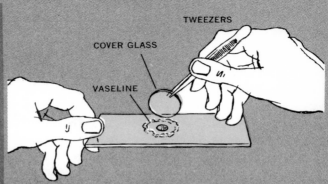

the slide wet side down on the cover glass and let them stand until the gelatin
hardens.

If you want to look at the tiny animals in pond or aquarium water, you
can make a Vaseline slide. With a toothpick, paint Vaseline on a slide in
a hollow square or circle the shape of a cover glass. Put a drop of water
containing specimens in the center and press a cover glass down gently
on top. The Vaseline seals the edge and keeps the water from evaporating.

Another way to prepare a pond-water slide is to make a slide "well."
Make holes in several thin squares of cardboard with a paper punch. Ap-
ply shellac to the cardboard squares and put them, one on top of the other,
in the center of a slide. After the shellac dries, put a drop of water in
the "well" and lay a cover glass on top.

You may wish to look at some of your slides again and again. One way
to make your slides permanent is to coat a dry specimen and slide with clear
nail polish or clear household cement. But a better way is to use Canada
balsam, a clear gum. Lay a dry specimen on a slide and cover it with a
drop of Canada balsam and a cover glass. The balsam hardens to preserve
the specimen.

Be sure to number or label your slide so that you don't forget what it is.
Write the name of the specimen, date and place of collection, and some
description in a notebook.

What To Look for

If you look at speciments of plant or animal life through your microscope,
you will often see tiny, thin-walled "boxes," or compartments, of various
shapes. These are *cells,* the "building blocks" of life. You can see rows
of them in a thin slice of onion skin or a slice of cork.

Some of the plants and animals you see may have only one cell. A
simple animal like *amoeba* is one cell that keeps changing in shape. Some-

times it splits into two new cells. More complicated animals and plants have many cells. Here are some things to find out when you look at living specimens through your microscope:

SIZE. Can you see the specimen without a microscope? How many times are you magnifying the specimen? How big is it?

SHAPE. Is the specimen round, oval, square, or more complicated in shape? Does it change shape? Are all the parts the same? Does one side look like the other side? Are all the cells alike?

ACTIVITY. Does the specimen move? Does it use "hairs," "arms," "legs," or other parts to move itself? Do any animals seem to be eating other animals? Are any cells splitting to form new cells?

STRUCTURE. Are there single cells or many cells? Can you see cell walls, or things inside the cell walls? Are there "hairs," "arms," "legs," or openings around the outside of the specimen?

Looking at non-living things through a microscope can also be fun. Bits of soil, sand grains, particles scraped from rocks and minerals, crystals of table salt or other chemicals—such things reveal their structure under a microscope. You won't see any cells in such specimens, but you will discover their shape, color, size, smoothness, or roughness, how they fit together, and whether light shines through them, for example.

There's an endless variety of different things that you can examine through a microscope. Scientists use their microscopes to identify specimens, to compare different specimens of the same kind, and to study the changes that take place in living and non-living things. You can do all of these things with your microscope ■

—Nature and Science

THE MAN WHO FIRST SAW "ANIMALCULES"

The man who gets credit for the first satisfactory microscope had little education. But Anton van Leeuwenhoek, a cloth merchant of Delft, Holland, made lenses that magnified up to about 250 times and revealed objects as small as four-thousandths of an inch in size. During his life (1632–1723), he spent more than 50 years studying "animalcules," as he called little animals, and plants. He found his specimens in canal water, mud, flies, frogs, and the soil.

A suspicious man, Leeuwenhoek kept his best instruments hidden and his greatest discoveries secret from most people. But he did reveal his work to a famous group of scientists, the Royal Society of London, who honored him by making him a member. Nearly all the experiments he did after that are described in letters that he wrote to the Society.

Make Your Own Microscope

■ Here's how to make a simple microscope that's small and light enough to take on trips, yet powerful enough to make things look 80 times bigger than they are. Most of the things you need to make a microscope like this are in most people's homes, so it may cost you as little as 20 cents (for a penlight bulb) to make one. The diagram on page 57 shows how the microscope is made.

How To Make Your Microscope

Begin by sawing the piece of wood into four pieces (*see diagram for sizes*). Smooth the sides and ends with sandpaper so they will fit together tightly.

Next, drill holes of the proper size in the places shown by dotted lines in the diagram. Some of these holes will be where a screw or nail goes to hold two pieces together, so it's important to drill these holes in exactly the right place. To make sure the holes are right, hold the two pieces of wood together so you can drill both holes at once. Mark each piece of wood so that later on you'll be able to remember where the pieces are supposed to go.

If you don't have drill bits of the right size, make the holes by hammering in nails that have the proper wideness.

Glue aluminum foil over the top of the one-inch-square block, and about $\frac{1}{8}$ of an inch down each side. Be sure the foil is smooth so that it will reflect as much light as possible. (If you have a glass mirror that is small enough to be glued on the wood block, it will work even better.)

To hold the mirror block under the lens in your microscope, use a piece of coat-hanger wire. Cut a piece 4½ inches long, and bend it to the shape shown in the diagram. Push the bent end into the hole in the side of the block.

Now, using Duco cement or Elmer's glue, glue the wood blocks together as shown. Put in the nails and set the frame aside to dry.

While it is drying, you can bend two paper clips into slide holders. Shape them with a pair of pliers, then screw the holders into place.

Next, glue the spool under the $\frac{7}{32}$-inch hole through the top of the microscope frame so that you can see down through the hole in the frame and the hole in the spool. Paint the inside of the spool and hole with flat black paint. To make the lens holder, use your tin shears or old scissors to cut from your tin can lid—or from a piece of copper flashing—a strip 3¾ inches by ⅝ of an inch. Drill a neat $\frac{7}{32}$-inch hole in one end, and file or scrape it smooth. Drive a nail through the opposite end to make the ⅛-inch screw hole. When driving the nail, lay the strip on a piece of wood that you don't need. This will help make the hole neat and keep you from damaging your work area. If you use plastic instead of metal for the strip, drill both holes slowly so you won't crack the plastic.

The lens at the tip of the penlight bulb is what you will use for the microscope lens. To get this lens, you must first cut the metal base off the bulb, using the shears. *Be sure to cover the bulb with a piece of heavy cloth when you're cutting, to keep the pieces from flying across the room.* (Another way to cut off the base is with a screwdriver and a hammer. But there's more chance of splitting the lens this way.) Use pliers to break off tiny pieces of the bulb until you are within $\frac{1}{16}$ of an inch from the lens.

To glue the lens into the hole in the strip, put a little Ambroid or Duco cement around the rough part of the lens and press it against the underside of the strip. The smooth dome of the lens will be sticking through the strip. Let the cement dry. Then paint a black rim around the domed side of the lens so light won't be able to come up around its sides. The paint should go a very little way up the sides of the dome to cut down glare from the side. Instead of paint, you can use black sticky tape with a hole cut in it.

Stick the straight end of the mirror holder into the hole in the frame as shown in the diagram. Then screw the lens holder onto the top piece of wood, with the lens right over the hole. Make sure the strip is flat against the wood. Also make sure there's no dirt, cement, or paint on the top or bottom of the lens. Use a Q-Tip, or a toothpick with cotton wrapped around the end, to clean the underside of the lens.

Using Your Microscope

If you want to look at something through your microscope, put the object on a glass slide or a strip of clear plastic about 1 by 3 inches, then put it under the lens. (The slide holders will hold the glass or plastic in place.)

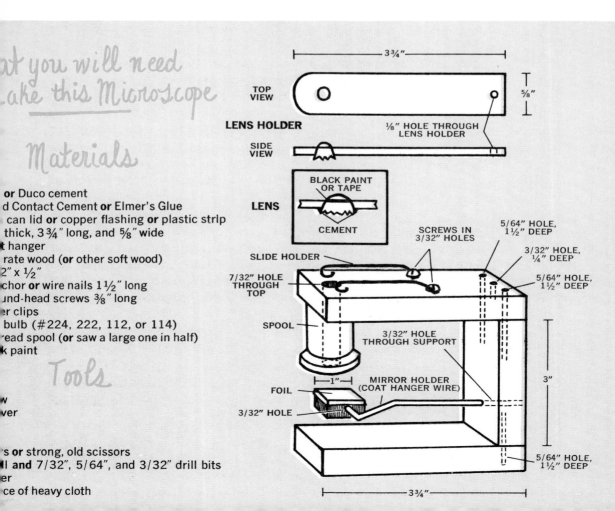

at you will need
ake this Microscope

Materials

or Duco cement
d Contact Cement or Elmer's Glue
can lid or copper flashing or plastic strip
thick, 3¾" long, and ⅝" wide
t hanger
rate wood (or other soft wood)
2" x ½"
chor or wire nails 1½" long
und-head screws ⅜" long
er clips
bulb (#224, 222, 112, or 114)
read spool (or saw a large one in half)
k paint

Tools

w
ver

s or strong, old scissors
l and 7/32, 5/64, and 3/32" drill bits
er
ce of heavy cloth

Look through the lens. Rock your mirror back and forth. How does the picture change? Can you see clearly what you put on your slide? If not, you must move the lens to get a sharper picture. Lay a nail or thin piece of wood under the lens holder at about its middle. Now, while looking through the lens, move the nail or wood slowly toward the lens, then toward the opposite end of the strip. How does the picture change as you move the nail forward and backward? Move your eye closer to the lens, then farther away. How does the picture change?

Put a very thin slice of onion under the lens. Look at it. Now put a slightly thicker slice under the lens. Look again. Do you see it as clearly? Move the mirror mount. What happens? Raise and lower the lens. What happens?

You can take this little microscope with you on hikes and nature trips. If you come to a pool of water that looks perfectly clear, take a drop and put it under your lens. You may be amazed at the creatures you find in a "clear" drop of water ■

—Nature and Science

TIPS ON SEEING CLEARLY WITH YOUR HOMEMADE MICROSCOPE

For a very good light, put a small lamp with a shade and bulb (25–60 watts) flat on the table close to the microscope. Bright sunlight or a strong flashlight also works well.

With the light shining full on the mirror (or aluminum foil), look through the lens. Tilt the mirror until you get all the light you can.

Make sure that you put the slide on the microscope so that the object is over the hole in the spool. When it is in position, clip it firm.

Does the closeness of your eye to the lens make a difference in what you see? Try different distances. If you wear glasses, you may see better through the microscope without them. Start with the lens almost touching the object. Move the lens up slowly until the object is clear. Use the nail or piece of wood to move the lens up and down ever so little. Sometimes your finger can give just the needed pressure. (If you move the lens up and down a lot, the strip loosens. To keep it near the object, put a strong elastic band around the other end of the microscope.)

You can get rid of almost all air bubbles by removing the cover slip, then putting it on again and pressing firmly. If you see shadows, try adjusting the mirror, the light, and the lens until the shadows disappear. A blurred image usually means a dirty lens. Clean the lens with wet tissue on the end of a toothpick; dry it with dry tissue the same way.

Measuring with a Microscope

■Imagine that you were only the size of your thumb! What a strange world this would be. The sight of your pet cat would terrify you as much as coming face to face with a dinosaur.

It might be fun to enter the world of the very small—as long as you can return at your own choosing. However, you needn't become a Tom Thumb or Thumbalina to explore the world of the very small. The lens of a microscope can be your keyhole for viewing the micro-world.

Strange things happen to you when you enter this micro-world. You lose all sense of size. The head of an insect can appear larger than an elephant's. When you view an insect in your normal world, you compare its size with objects around you. An insect is usually smaller than a pencil. On the other hand, most insects are larger than a grain of sand. In the normal world you have many standards for comparing size.

This is not true in the micro-world. When you look through a microscope you often see only one object. You have no way of comparing the object with those around it.

You need a standard to take along on your adventures into the micro-world. One standard is a foot. Your ruler is one foot long. This unit is much too large for many objects. Suppose you wanted to measure the length of your pencil. You would need a smaller unit such as the inch. An inch is divided into even smaller units. These standards are all much too large to use when you enter the micro-world.

A giant of the micro-world is about the size of the head of a pin. You can imagine the problem of selecting a standard unit so small that it would take a thousand such units to cover the width of the period at the end of this sentence.

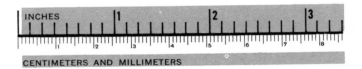

If you have a clear plastic ruler, you probably have all the tools you need for measuring size in the micro-world. Many such rulers contain two scales. One scale is the familiar inch-foot scale. The other is the *metric* scale.

The numbers on the metric scale show a unit called the *centimeter*. It takes about two and one-half of these to equal one inch. The centimeter is divided into ten smaller units called *millimeters*. The millimeter (mm.) is

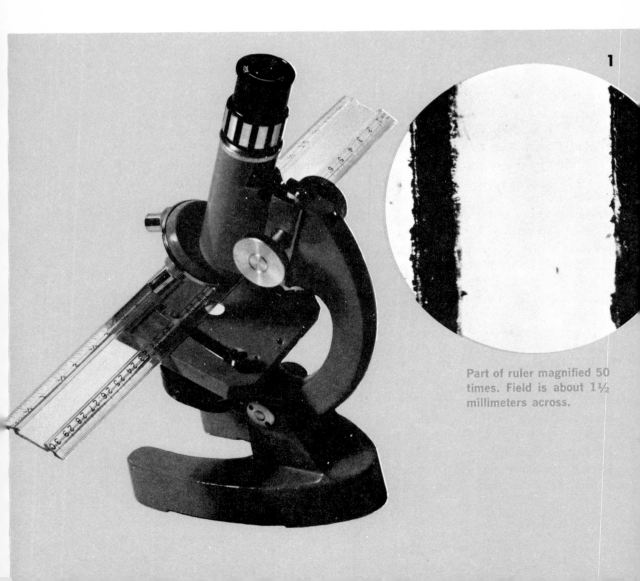

Part of ruler magnified 50 times. Field is about 1½ millimeters across.

the standard unit for most microscopic measurements. How large an area can you see through a microscope? Here's how to use your ruler and see.

Measuring with Millimeters

The area that you view through the eyepiece of the microscope is called the *field*. The size of the field changes as you change magnification. For instance, under low magnification you may see the entire leg of a fly. Under higher magnification, perhaps only a part of the end of the foot is visible.

The problem then is to measure the size of the field for the different magnifications. For low magnification, select the lowest power eyepiece and objective lens. The lenses are usually marked with their power of magnification. An eyepiece of five power (5X) and an objective lens of ten power (10X) gives a total magnification of 50 power.

The first step in measuring the size of the field is to place the clear plastic ruler on the stage, or platform, of the microscope in such a position

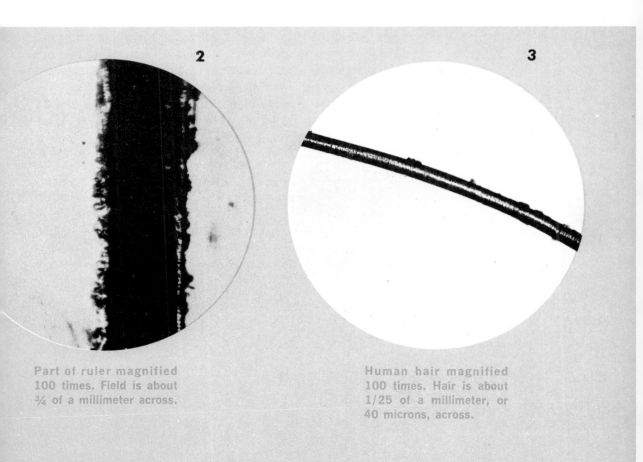

2   3

Part of ruler magnified
100 times. Field is about
¾ of a millimeter across.

Human hair magnified
100 times. Hair is about
1/25 of a millimeter, or
40 microns, across.

that the millimeter scale is directly in line with the lenses. Turn the focusing knob so that the lower (objective) lens almost touches the ruler. Then, as you view the ruler through the eyepiece, slowly turn the focusing knob so that the objective lens moves up from the stage. (Always focus by *raising* the objective lens to keep from striking and damaging it.)

When the ruler is focused clearly, you should see the markings on the ruler somewhat like the markings shown in photo 1, page 60.

Since the distance between each mark represents one millimeter, the field in this example is about $1\frac{1}{2}$ millimeters across. If you rotate the barrel so you are using a 20X objective with your 5X eyepiece, your total magnification would be 100 power. The field is about $\frac{3}{4}$ of a millimeter across when viewed under 100X magnification. *(See photo 2 on page 61.)*

Now, suppose you want to measure the thickness of a human hair. Place a hair on a slide and then cover the hair with a drop of water. Hold the hair in place by lowering a cover glass over it.

When viewed through a microscope, you can see that a hair is much less than a millimeter in width. The one shown in photo 3 on page 61 seems to be about 1/25 of a millimeter.

Suppose, in your mind, that you divided a millimeter into a thousand equal parts. Since these parts are very small, let's call them *microns*. A micron then is one-thousandth of a millimeter. The hair is $\frac{1}{25}$ of a millimeter in thickness, or 40 microns, since $\frac{1}{25}$ of a thousand is 40. Is your hair that thick?

Now that you know how to measure with a microscope, try to find the size of different objects. You might try to measure a fly's eye or a salt crystal. Can you think of other things to measure with a microscope? ∎

—*Raymond E. Barrett*

PROJECT

Get some hairs from your friends, or from members of your family. Look at the hairs under a microscope. Are dark hairs thicker than light colored ones? Is straight hair thicker than curly hair? Compare your hair with that of older people. Does hair thickness change with age? You might examine hairs from dogs and cats. How do they differ from human hair?

The Ways of Insects

Mealworm Watching

■ Are you a birdwatcher? If not, you probably know people in your neighborhood who spend hours on the lookout for interesting kinds of birds.

This chapter will tell you how to become a mealworm watcher. At first glance, mealworms may seem pretty dull compared to watching sea gulls or hawks, but you will soon find that mealworms can be a good deal more fascinating than you might suspect. Besides, they are far easier to take care of than birds, and you can do your mealworm watching whenever it is convenient for you.

Watching mealworms is not just a hobby; it can be a kind of real scientific research. Hundreds of scientists around the world spend all their time watching animals—everything from worms to gorillas—trying to figure out how the animals behave, how the animals react to such things as heat and cold and hunger and to other animals. The things they learn from their observations may be useful—for example, how to control harmful insects, how to keep wild animals from being wiped out, how to understand the human brain better.

To become a mealworm watcher, you will need:

1. Mealworms. You may find mealworms under a rotten log, but this is difficult and you probably won't find them except in the summer. Your best bet is to try the local pet store, which probably will have mealworms

Shine a flashlight on a mealworm. What does it do?

on hand since they are often used as food for chameleons or toads. They should not cost more than a penny or two each. If you can't get them nearby, you might order them through a biological supply house (*see list on page 122*). Mealworms, by the way, are the young (*larvae*) of a kind of black beetle.

2. *Food.* Breakfast cereals such as corn flakes or wheat flakes make a good food for your mealworms. They live right in the cereal and feed on it too. Every couple of days, add a banana skin and some lettuce; this keeps the cereal moist. But don't let the cereal get too wet or it will get moldy.

3. *Container.* You will need one container, perhaps a glass jar with about one-half inch of cereal in the bottom.

Can Mealworms Be Made To Back Up?

Certain things will make a mealworm back up. There are several things you might try: putting an obstacle in its path; tapping it on the head with a straw; putting a drop of water on its head; putting your finger in front of it; shining a flashlight on it; holding a hot bulb near it; blowing on it from a couple of inches away. Make a chart like this:

What was done	Times Tried	Mealworm Continues Forward	Mealworm Goes Backward	Rank
Flashlight ½ inch away	101	52	49	

65

Each method should be tried many times. When you have finished, see which method was most effective in making the mealworm back up. Mark it "1st" in the column headed "Rank," mark the second most effective method "2nd," and so on.

Do Mealworms See?

Put a mealworm in the middle of an empty test box. (Use an empty shoe box or cigar box with a strip of transparent tape around the rim so it is too slippery for the worm to climb out.) Block the worm's forward motion by holding a mirror across its path. What does the mealworm do? Why? Do the same thing with a piece of cardboard. Does the mealworm act as it did when the mirror blocked its way?

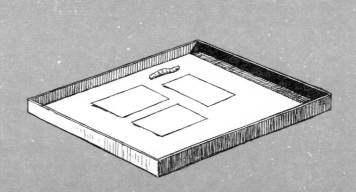

Pieces of cardboard laid flat make "walls" for mealworms.

Next, flash a beam of light from a flashlight at the worm. Is the mealworm motionless? Does it move? Keep a score sheet handy to mark down your findings.

Place a block of wood several inches thick in the middle of the box. What does your mealworm do? Next put three pieces of cardboard inside the box, but set them with spaces between each piece. Do you believe mealworms can see? Can you find any eyes?

Do Mealworms Feel?

Tap gently on the head of a mealworm with the tip of a pencil. What does your worm do? Take a straw and carefully touch the worm. Now gently blow through the straw and watch the actions of your mealworm. What do your investigations tell you? What else can you try?

Put a mealworm in an empty box and let it explore. From watching the worm, you will notice that it tends to follow "walls." How do you suppose mealworms sense the presence of a wall? How would you follow a wall? You would see it. But suppose you were blind; what would help you then? Your arm or the side of your body could be used to find the wall and keep in touch to follow it. What would a mealworm do?

To find out whether a mealworm must see the wall in order to follow it, you might test the worm by putting its box in the dark. But then how will you know where it goes? If you scatter a little powder over the bottom of the box, the worm should leave a trail as it moves about.

You will have to examine a mealworm's body to find out how it follows a wall without seeing. Use a magnifying glass or a microscope. What do you see? You find a pair of pointed antennae on its head, hooks on the end of each leg, and fine "hairs" on the legs and underside of the body. One or more of these structures could serve as a touch-sensing device. Which did your mealworm use? Try your test on another mealworm and watch its motions through a magnifying glass. What did it tell you? Investigate several mealworms' actions. Write down your observations and compare them. Did all the mealworms tested use the same body structure to sense and follow the wall?

Why Does a Mealworm Stay Under the Corn Flakes?

Can you figure out why the mealworms stay in the cereal? Here are some possible reasons: because it is their food supply; because it is dark; because they "like" a weight on their backs; because it is quiet; because it has an odor that is pleasing for them. Can you figure out a way of checking these theories?

You might check the "weight" theory by putting something other than cereal on the mealworms' backs. Does it have the same effect? Try something that is about the same weight as cereal but lets light through—shredded cellophane, for example.

Do mealworms stay in the cereal because of the darkness? Try putting cereal into a completely dark box and see whether the mealworms still linger in the food.

To see if mealworms eat the cereal, you might try some other kind of food and test three or four mealworms, each in its own little matchbox, with just a few flakes of the kind of food you want to test. Do mealworms prefer corn flakes over wheat flakes or oat flakes? Put a flake of each cereal (all about the same size) into a box with several worms and see which is eaten first.

Can you think of other ways to study the behavior of these animals? ■

—*David Webster*

67

The World of the Housefly

■ (SWAT!) They walk around on your food, leaving germs which they carry on their feet. (SWAT!!) They walk on your walls and windows, leaving spots and specks wherever they go. (SWAT!!!) Nobody loves them. Why, then, would you want to know anything about houseflies? One reason, to control them better. Also, what we learn about flies will help us understand how other insects, and even other kinds of animals, live and behave.

Houseflies are easy to raise. In a small box and a small jar you can watch the life cycle of a fly. As you do, many interesting questions about them will pop into mind. Perhaps you can plan experiments to help find answers.

A cage for adult flies must be designed so that the flies will have food, water, and air. There must be some way to get the flies into the cage, and a way to get them out. If flies are to reproduce, they must also have a suitable place for laying eggs. The cage must not let the flies escape or let other insects get in. You may be surprised to find what small cracks flies can squeeze through. Diagrams on pages 70-71 show how to make a cage for flies.

Before you make a cage you should make some food for the flies. In a cup or small dish, mix one teaspoon of powdered milk with one teaspoon of confectioners' sugar. Stir in water, drop by drop, until all of the mixture is moist. Use as little water as you can. Spread the paste on a piece of paper, dividing it into two or three small patches, each about the size of a quarter. Set these food patches aside to dry.

Making the Cage

You will need a clean, dry, milk container (one-quart size is best). Find a glass jar, also clean and dry, whose top is smaller than the bottom of the milk container. You can use a $7\frac{3}{4}$-ounce baby-food jar or a small jelly jar. Hold the top of the jar against the bottom of the milk carton and trace carefully around it. With a sharp cutting tool, carefully cut out the circle you have drawn. (Keep your cut about $\frac{1}{16}$ inch inside the line.) The top of your jar should fit *snugly* into the hole. Once you have tested the fit, don't keep moving the jar into and out of the hole, because this will stretch the hole. Put the jar aside now, but save it. You will need it later for the flies to lay their eggs in.

Cut off the top of the milk box and make the edges even, then bend the top of the box until it is round instead of square.

Next, make a cone through which flies can enter the cage. Use a stiff paper (such as construction paper, heavy wrapping paper, or the cover of a magazine). Roll a cone about 6 inches long, 2 to $2\frac{1}{2}$ inches wide at the base, and with a hole at the pointed end big enough to slide a pencil into. Fasten the cone together with tape, staples, or both.

Now, the cone must be fastened to the box. To do this, cut a slit like the one that is shown in diagram 3, about 2 inches from the top of the carton. Bend the flap outward, and push the cone into the hole with the point aiming partly up. Fasten the cone to the carton and to the flap with tape. Cover any spaces around the edges with tape.

By this time the fly food should be dry. Cut out a scrap of paper with one of the cakes of food on it. Fasten it with tape to the inside of the box.

Now cover the bottom and the top of the carton. Use a piece of plastic food wrap, or any transparent plastic, to cover the bottom. Pull the plastic around the bottom edges of the box and fasten it smoothly with tape. (See diagram 4.) Cover the top with a piece of old nylon stocking. A rubber band will hold the stocking in place.

The Water Supply

The flies will need a water supply. They will drink from a piece of sponge placed on top of the nylon stocking. To make a drinking hole in the stocking, paint a circle (about as big as a dime) in the center with nail polish. The hole can be cut after the nail polish has dried, and the ring of polish will keep the hole from getting larger. While the nail polish is drying you can get the sponge ready.

Cut a piece of sponge about $1\times1\times\frac{1}{2}$ inch. Wet it and squeeze it out, then wrap it in a piece of plastic food wrap (6 to 8 inches long) as shown in the diagram. Gently twist the plastic as near to the sponge as you can without squashing the sponge out of shape. Then put a strip of tape around each of the twisted places. With pointed scissors cut a small hole (about as big as a pencil) in each side of the plastic as shown in the diagram. Now cut a similar hole *inside* the nail polish circle on the stocking. Be sure to leave a border of nail polish around the hole. Now fix the sponge to the top of the milk carton, as shown in the first diagram.

Make sure that one hole in the plastic is over the hole in the stocking. You can look up through the bottom of the cage to line up the holes. Your

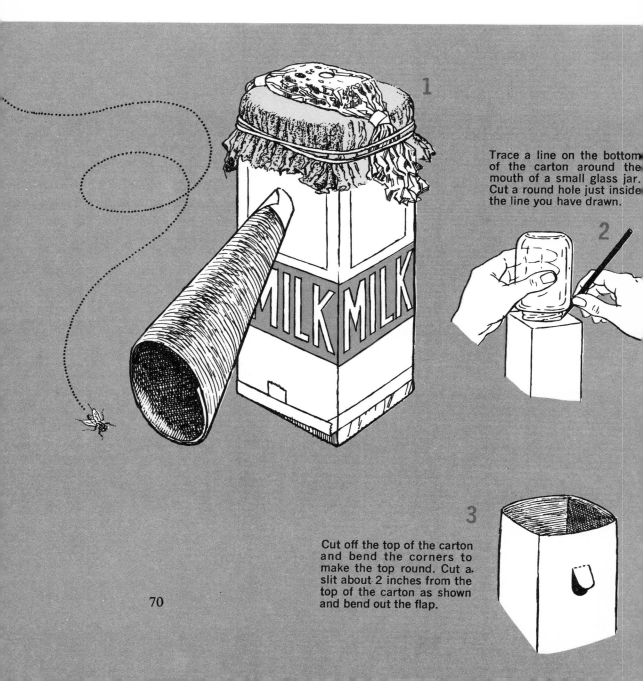

1

Trace a line on the bottom of the carton around the mouth of a small glass jar. Cut a round hole just inside the line you have drawn.

2

3

Cut off the top of the carton and bend the corners to make the top round. Cut a slit about 2 inches from the top of the carton as shown and bend out the flap.

70

cage is now finished.

Now it's time to catch flies! An easy way to catch flies is to pop a plastic cup over a fly on a window. Slip a card under the cup, and transfer the fly to a small plastic bag. Ask someone to hold the bag upside down for you. Then push the cup up into the bag and release the fly. It will probably go all the way up into the bag. Your helper can keep the first fly trapped in a corner while you put the second fly into the bag.

Catch about a dozen flies. You will almost surely have a mixture of males and females. (Since flies can spread some diseases, be sure to wash the plastic cup and your hands well when you have finished fly catching.)

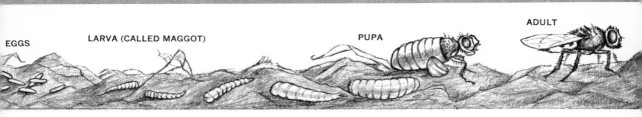

EGGS   LARVA (CALLED MAGGOT)   PUPA   ADULT

LIFE CYCLE OF THE HOUSEFLY

The housefly (*Musca domestica* is its scientific name) goes through four stages in its lifetime: 1) egg; 2) larva (also called maggot); 3) pupa; and 4) adult.

The first stages of development take place inside the egg. When the egg hatches, a *larva* crawls out. The wormlike fly larva does not have legs or wings. As it grows, it sheds its outer layer of skin twice. This is called *molting*. All insects molt. The large housefly larvae which have molted twice are the maggots which many of us have seen at some time.

When the larva stops growing, its skin becomes shorter and stiff, forming a barrel-shaped pupa case. Inside this case the *pupa* develops wings, legs, eyes, and other features which the larva did not have.

About 10 days to two weeks after the egg is laid, the adult fly pushes its way out of the pupa case. It is now ready to buzz into your kitchen and find its first meal as an adult.

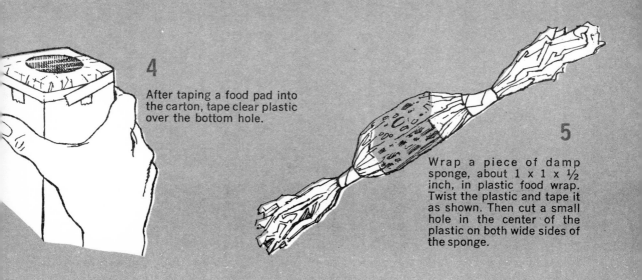

4
After taping a food pad into the carton, tape clear plastic over the bottom hole.

5
Wrap a piece of damp sponge, about 1 x 1 x ½ inch, in plastic food wrap. Twist the plastic and tape it as shown. Then cut a small hole in the center of the plastic on both wide sides of the sponge.

Before you put the flies in the cage, make sure that you have caught true houseflies. Here are two ways to get a good look at the flies: You can hold a fly tightly, but gently, between the folds of the plastic bag, then look at it carefully; or you can chill the flies for about 10 minutes in a refrigerator. This will slow them down long enough for you to observe them closely before they warm up.

When you have caught enough flies, slip the end of the plastic bag over the wide part of the cone of your cage. Gather it close around the cone so that the flies can't escape. You might want to tape the bag in place while the flies walk up through the funnel into the cage. If you want to hurry them, put the cage near a bright window, making sure that the small end of the funnel is toward the light. When the flies are all in, take off the plastic bag and stuff a wad of cotton or tissue paper into the funnel so that they can't escape. (Or remove the cone and cover the flap with tape.) With a

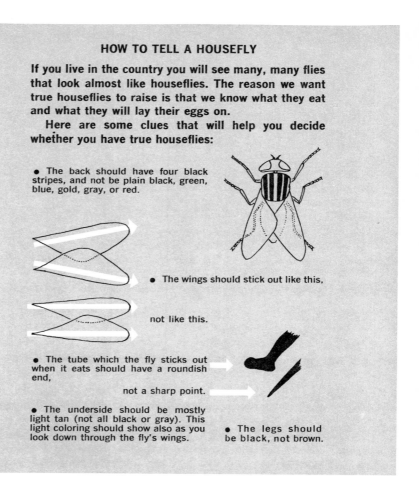

HOW TO TELL A HOUSEFLY

If you live in the country you will see many, many flies that look almost like houseflies. The reason we want true houseflies to raise is that we know what they eat and what they will lay their eggs on.

Here are some clues that will help you decide whether you have true houseflies:

● The back should have four black stripes, and not be plain black, green, blue, gold, gray, or red.

● The wings should stick out like this,

not like this.

● The tube which the fly sticks out when it eats should have a roundish end,

not a sharp point.

● The underside should be mostly light tan (not all black or gray). This light coloring should show also as you look down through the fly's wings.

● The legs should be black, not brown.

1 . . . When you put the flies into the plastic bag, or when you moved them from the bag to the cage, you were helped by the flies themselves. You saw that they usually flew or walked upward toward the light. Can you do an experiment to show which (if either) is more important—the upward direction or the light? (A cage that has clear plastic over the top as well as the bottom might be helpful. Also, a flashlight or mirror.)

2 . . . What scares a fly? If a fly is on the outside of a window, and you are on the inside, can you touch your hand to the glass opposite its feet? How close can you bring your finger to a fly that is standing on a screen or on the stocking that covers your fly cage? Can you bring your finger closer to a fly's tail, back, side, or head without scaring it? Is there any sort of noise that will make your flies move? What happens if you blow on them? Do flies behave differently at night than in daytime, when they are naturally most active?

3 . . . How many different kinds of flies live in your neighborhood?

4 . . . Collect one fly that is not a housefly. List as many differences as you can between a housefly and the other fly. If you were writing a book about identifying flies, would you be satisfied to describe a type of fly when you had looked at only one of its kind?

5 . . . Can you show whether adult flies like some foods better than others? To help you find out, make another cage like the one shown on page 70, but do not put a food patch inside of it. Cut a large window in the side opposite the entry cone, and tape clear plastic over the window. In the stocking, make a food hole as well as a water hole, and tape a patch of paper with a food cake on it over the hole. With a large round pencil, punch two holes just large enough for a jumbo drinking straw in each of the sides having neither the window nor the cone entry. Cover the holes temporarily with tape.

After the flies are in the cage, remove the cone and tape that hole closed. Provide water as before, through the sponge. Before making food tests, remove the patch of fly food, cover the food hole, and let the flies have only water for about a day. Then remove the sponge, cover the water hole, and put the cage on its side, window upward.

Cut holes in the middle of two jumbo drinking straws and put a bit of absorbent cotton into each hole. Moisten the cotton of one with water, the other with milk. Uncover the holes in the sides of the cage and insert the straws, trying not to let the liquid touch the side of the cage. Do the flies prefer milk to water? Test the flies with other choices of food, such as milk and sugar water, milk and salt water, honey water and bouillon. *Remember to give them nothing but water for one day before each test.* Do they prefer water with a little sugar or with a lot of sugar in it? Food in solid form or mixed with water? Can you find out what parts of a fly are able to taste?

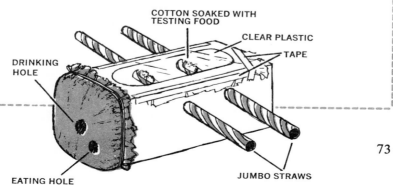

COTTON SOAKED WITH
TESTING FOOD

CLEAR PLASTIC

TAPE

DRINKING
HOLE

JUMBO STRAWS

EATING HOLE

73

medicine dropper or spoon, wet the sponge until it is almost dripping.

The flies can live for weeks in this cage. Every day that you can, you should add a little water to the sponge. If you add too much and it drips into the cage, do not add any more water until the puddle has dried. If you go away for a few days, or if it is extremely dry in your house, cover the cage loosely with a piece of plastic. This will help keep the sponge moist. If the flies die, even though they have food and water, it is probably because they are sick or old, or because they are not houseflies and do not have the kind of food they need.

Let the Flies Lay Eggs

Now you have a cage of lively flies. A few of the flies you caught— old ones or sick ones—may be dead by now. If some did die, try to catch a few more, so that you have at least a dozen lively ones.

Within about a week after the flies are caught and caged, they should be ready to lay eggs. Houseflies lay eggs where yeast is growing. The eggs hatch in about a day, and the *larvae* (maggots) crawl out of the eggs and eat the yeast. In the "wild," common places where flies find yeast are on

This wax model shows in detail the body of a housefly maggot. The head is at the pointed end and the small bumps serve as "legs."

74

garbage and manure. But you can grow your own yeast on dog food. You will need dried dog food, such as Purina Dog Chow (do not get any of the gravy-flavored dog foods).

Put about 1½ inches of the dried dog food into the glass breeding jar that fits your cage. (If your jar is quite small, make it only one-third full.) After measuring the amount, pour the food out again into a small bowl and add just enough hot water to cover the pieces. Let it stand for 10 minutes or more. While you wait, mix ¼ teaspoon of dried yeast and about ½ teaspoon of warm water, and let this stand. When 10 minutes are up, pour off any of the water that has not soaked into the dog food. Now sprinkle the moistened yeast on top of the dog food and mix gently. Spoon the food back into the breeding jar. Do not pack it down. This mixture is your maggot food.

Now you are ready to attach the breeding jar to the cage. To do this, place the cage on a piece of cardboard. Have a helper hold the cage steady while you carefully take off the tape that holds the bottom plastic on. Slide the plastic out without lifting the cage from the cardboard. Place the cage and cardboard over the jar of maggot food so that the hole in the bottom of the cage is lined up right over the jar. Now have your helper pull the cardboard away, and quickly press the cage onto the jar. Tape

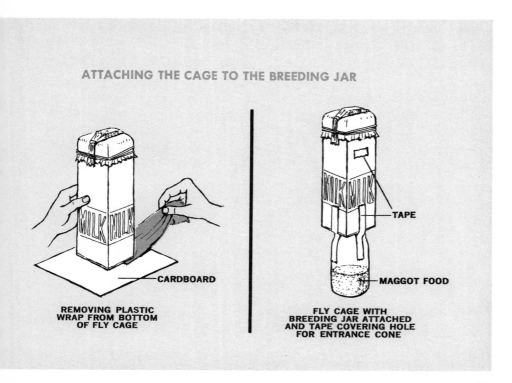

ATTACHING THE CAGE TO THE BREEDING JAR

CARDBOARD

REMOVING PLASTIC
WRAP FROM BOTTOM
OF FLY CAGE

TAPE

MAGGOT FOOD

FLY CAGE WITH
BREEDING JAR ATTACHED
AND TAPE COVERING HOLE
FOR ENTRANCE CONE

75

the cage to the jar, and if there are cracks, seal them with tape. The flies can now lay eggs on the maggot food. When the temperature is between about 80° and 90° F., the flies will lay lots of eggs. In cold weather try to keep your flies just near enough to a radiator.

Watching for Larvae

Housefly eggs are white and are shaped like hot dogs. They are about as long as a pinhead is wide. The flies will lay their eggs in cracks and between chunks of the maggot food. Because the eggs are so small, and are usually well hidden, you may not see them at all.

The first sign of life in your maggot food will probably be some mold. Mold usually forms in two to four days. At about the same time, or a little sooner, you should be able to see some small larvae. You may now remove the jar from the box. Do this out of doors if you don't want to keep the adult flies in the cage. If you want to keep them, use the cardboard slide again and cover the bottom of the cage again with plastic food wrap.

Cover the maggot jar with two thicknesses of nylon stocking held on with a rubber band. If there are enough larvae they will destroy most of the mold. If a week goes by and you still don't see larvae, but lots of mold, empty the jar in the toilet. Prepare a new mixture of maggot food in a new jar, set the cage of flies over the jar, and try again. (Don't try to wash out the old jar. It is very hard to clean it well enough to remove all traces of the mold.)

The larvae grow very quickly in a warm room. In a week they may be half an inch long. To get a good look at a maggot, fish one out with a twig or pipe cleaner and put it on a damp paper towel. Can you see how it moves?

The maggots usually crawl up the side of the jar as the maggot food becomes wetter. When this happens, add about ¼ inch of sand, sawdust, or crumbled dried leaves to the jar. If a maggot goes all the way to the top and burrows through one layer of stocking, add a third layer of stocking. Always keep two layers ahead of the maggots.

But you may want the maggots to climb more so that you can see them better. Remove the stocking and make the jar airtight with a cover of plastic food wrap held on with a rubber band. In about an hour the maggots will start climbing. Put the stocking cover back on after you have finished watching the maggots. Why do you suppose this makes the maggots climb?

Watching for Pupae and Adults

About a week after the maggots first appear, they will move out of the moist layers of the food to the dry, top layer and turn into *pupae*. The pupal cases are about ⅜ inch long. If you watch them carefully you will see them turn from yellow to brown. Within the pupal case the pupa changes into an adult fly.

While the pupae are changing, you may leave the pupal cases where they are or put them into another jar. Be sure to keep the jar covered! Hatching will start in about two weeks. The newly hatched flies can be used to fill another feeding cage. In this way you can keep your fly investigations going all year ■

—Nancy Kent Ziebur

INVESTIGATIONS

1 . . . On a warm day, put a jar of fresh maggot food outdoors. After a day or two cover it with a double layer of nylon stocking and put it where you can watch for larvae. How many different kinds of flies eventually appear?

2 . . . Flies will lay eggs on a small patch of special food and produce *clumps* of eggs that are easy to see. To prepare this special food—"fermenting maggot food"—simply let some regular maggot food stand for two to four days in a jar tightly covered with plastic. Next, put a spoonful of fermenting maggot food onto a piece of plastic. Remove the sponge from the fly cage and turn the cage upside down so that the hole in the stocking is against the food. After one day look for eggs on the patch of fermenting maggot food. If there are none, repeat the whole procedure after about a week. The fermenting maggot food can be kept covered in the refrigerator.

3 . . . What happens to maggots if their jar is covered tightly with plastic for a long time? How many different explanations of the results can you think of? What experiments would help you choose between the different explanations? You may wish to divide your larvae among several jars. Prepare new jars of fermenting maggot food and add the larvae.

4 . . . When a jar of maggots is put in a warm, sunny spot, the maggots usually are more active than when they are in a cool, dim room. Can you tell whether the maggots are responding to the light, or to the heat? Are there other possible explanations? What about the effect of the light or the heat on the yeast?

5 . . . Do maggots respond to different substances that they meet? Dampen two paper towels. On one towel sprinkle a line of sugar to form a circle. On the other make a circle of pepper. Put a few maggots into each circle. Do the maggots crawl out of both circles right away? Try some other foods and chemicals. If you wish to test a liquid, such as insect repellant, dip a piece of string into the liquid and arrange it to form a circle on a damp paper towel. For comparison use a circle of string wet with water.

6 . . . What animals eat flies and maggots? Try feeding maggots to a pet bird, turtle, fish, or mouse. If there is a place near to you where sparrows or pigeons gather, see if they will eat maggots. Will they eat pupae? (Uneaten maggots and pupae should be destroyed—by squashing or drowning in soapy water—lest they become adults.)

7 . . . At which stages in its life cycle do you think a fly can best resist cold weather? Try keeping flies, eggs, maggots, or pupae in a refrigerator, or in a freezer, for an hour, a day, a week or two. You can try keeping them outdoors if the weather is cold. Are they killed? If you try this, be sure to keep part of your living stock at room temperature for comparison.

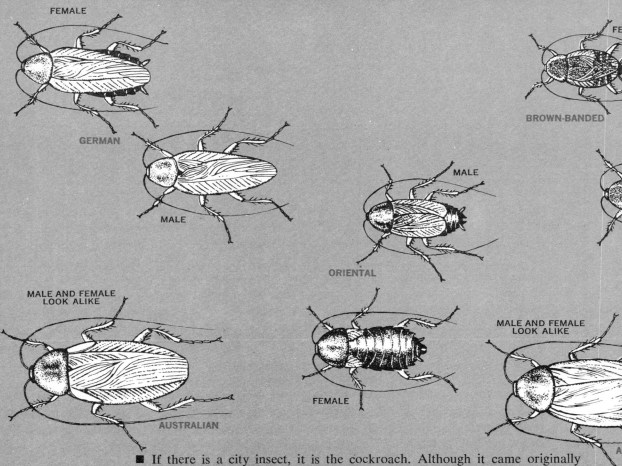

FEMALE
GERMAN
MALE
MALE
FE
BROWN-BANDED
ORIENTAL
MALE AND FEMALE LOOK ALIKE
AUSTRALIAN
FEMALE
MALE AND FEMALE LOOK ALIKE

■ If there is a city insect, it is the cockroach. Although it came originally from the tropics, the roach has traveled all over the world as a stowaway. It even thrives in the Arctic (in heated buildings). Every large city swarms with roaches, and urban housewives usually aren't entirely free of them for very long.

It is misleading to speak of "the roach," as though there were only one. In fact, there are about 3,500 kinds (*species*) in the world. Most of them are outdoor insects in the tropics. Only a few kinds of roaches live indoors. About half a dozen are at home throughout the continental United States. (Alaska has only one species; Hawaii, being tropical, has many more species that do not occur on the mainland.)

International Insects

The most widespread of these pests is the German roach, a pale tan species about half-an-inch long when fully grown. (Germans call this insect the French roach!) The American roach, a chestnut-brown species an inch-

and-a-half long, is almost as common. The broad, dark brown, short-winged kind is called the oriental roach in the United States and the black beetle in England. (It is not really black, and not a beetle!)

The Australian roach is like the American, but a little smaller, with a yellow streak on the "shoulder" of each front wing. The brown-banded roach resembles the German, but the female has short wings. The gray-brown Madeira roach is bigger than the American. It lives only in cities visited by ships from tropic ports.

Although many roaches are named for places from which they supposedly came, the names may all be mistaken. Possibly all the common house roaches began in Africa, but that is far from certain. They have lived with man so long and have been so widely spread in the belongings of traveling people that their original homes may never be known. The German roach may well have come from Asia before history began. Whatever their origin, roaches have lived in cities as long as people have. Before that they shared the huts of villagers and the caves and tents of even earlier men. Not that they care much for people. They just like what people have to eat.

Roaches, like people, are *omnivores*—eaters of both plant and animal food. But roaches eat a greater variety of foods than most humans. Plant or animal, living or dead—anything that will stand still and be eaten is food for roaches. However, they much prefer moist, soft substances, such as garbage.

They drop their own wastes wherever they happen to be feeding. Many human diseases are caused by "germs" that can pass uninjured through the digestive system of a roach. The insects may spread infection by picking up "germs" in the sewer and leaving them in the kitchen. Polio and typhoid fever are among the diseases roaches may carry. However, no one has yet proved that roaches have ever played an important part in the sudden spread of any disease.

Why Roaches Keep in Touch

You have only to look at a cockroach to know that it lives in crevices. It is flat and slippery, with strong pushing spines on its legs and long, thread-like antennae that "smell" the outside world before the insect leaves its shelter.

Roaches are *thigmotactic*—they can rest quietly only when in contact with something. The more surfaces of its body a roach has touching something, the more secure it seems to feel. House roaches hide by day in cellars and closets, behind and under articles of furniture, inside radios, electric clocks, and television sets, and in a thousand crannies that a housekeeper never thinks to examine.

At night they come out and search for supper and a drink of water. Roaches need a lot of water, unless their food is very wet. This is why they are so much more likely to be seen in the kitchen, bathroom, or laundry

79

Cockroaches are good laboratory animals, easy to get and to care for, little enough to keep in a small space but large enough to handle and to watch without using a magnifying glass. If you watch captive roaches carefully, you will see them doing things that will suggest experiments. For instance:

● If there are hiding places in their cage, roaches will stay hidden all day and come out to feed at night. What happens if you keep the insects always in darkness or always in light? Do they stay on their usual schedule? If not, how long does it take for their schedule to break down, and how soon does it come back when you expose them to the normal cycle of light and darkness? If you find that the roaches stay on their usual schedule, see whether you can change their hours of hiding and hunting by changing the hours of light and darkness.

● Roaches hide in dark crevices. Which is more important to the roach, the darkness or the tight fit? If you offer the insects a snug shelter made of transparent plastic, and a dark, roomy shelter that is round so that only the roaches' feet can touch any surface, which will they choose?

END MAY BE CLOSED   OPEN AT BOTH ENDS

SNUG, TRANSPARENT SHELTER   DARK, ROOMY SHELTER

● Does a roach have a special "home" to which it returns every morning? Give your roaches several identical hiding places, such as small boxes. Mark the insects with numbers painted on their backs in waterproof ink so that you can tell them apart. Examine each box every morning to see which roaches are in it.

The better you get to know your roaches, the more questions you will ask yourself about them, and the more experiments you will be able to think of to help answer your questions.

room than in a bedroom or living room. Because so many places offer shelter to roaches, it is very hard to reach all of them with an insect-killing poison (*insecticide*).

Since roaches are so abundant, people think they reproduce rapidly, but that is not true. Many species need at least a year to produce a new generation of adults. The number of young produced by one female roach in her lifetime is not great when compared with many other kinds of insects.

You may have seen a female roach with her egg capsule protruding from the rear of her body. The capsule looks like a tiny purse. Some species carry the capsule inside their bodies until the eggs hatch and the young are born alive.

The young roaches look like adults, except that they have no wings. During their growth they shed their skins many times. Immediately after shedding, the insect is milk white. People who see a roach in a new skin are likely to mistake it for an *albino*—an animal that stays white all of its life, even though that is not the usual color for its species. But if you keep the roach for half a day, you will see it gradually change to the normal color.

Even though most people dislike them, roaches are of a very old and distinguished family. Three hundred million years ago, they were the most common animals on land. They have changed very little since then. In the time of the dinosaurs, they were already as old as the dinosaurs would be now if they still existed. A family so tough and so adaptable is likely to be with us a while longer. Perhaps the last living creature on the earth will be a roach ■

—Alice Gray

CATCHING AND CARING FOR COCKROACHES

You can make a roach trap using a half-pint bottle with a screw cap. The best cap is the two-piece kind—a flat cover with a screw rim to hold it in place. You use only the rim. If you can't get that, cut most of the top out of an ordinary lid with a pair of tinsnips. You will also need a scrap of window screening about as big as half a sheet of letter paper, to make the funnel part of the trap. (Screening lets the smell of the bait in the trap reach the insects.)

SCREENING

STAPLES   BAIT

Roll a piece of paper into a cone. Fit the cone into the mouth of the bottle. Adjust it until the cone's point reaches about halfway to the bottom of the bottle while the top fits the mouth tightly. Fasten the paper in this shape with sticky tape, then draw a pencil line around the cone at the top of the jar. Press the cone flat and cut it open along one fold. Trim the top about half an inch above the pencil line. Then use this pattern to cut your screening, with about half an inch extra at the side to allow for overlap.

Roll the screen into a cone and fasten it with staples, or sew it shut with a big needle and a piece of string. Cut off the tip to make a hole big enough for a roach to get through. Fit the funnel into the jar and turn the very top down over the top of the jar. Screw on the cover to hold it in place. Bait your trap with a piece of very ripe banana or a little stale beer on a scrap of paper towel. Lay the trap on its side against a wall behind or under something in the cellar, or wherever you know that roaches live. (If you don't know where there are any, ask the manager of a supermarket or school cafeteria for permission to put the trap in a back room.) Leave it overnight.

A gallon mayonnaise jar from a restaurant will make a fine cage for roaches. Cut out the center of the lid and put in a piece of wire screening, cut to fit. Give the insects a crushed paper towel in which to hide. Feed them dry cat food crushed to powder. Make them a drinking fountain out of a small, wide-mouthed bottle or test tube. (Just fill the bottle with water and plug it tightly with a wad of wet cotton, so that the water will not run out when you lay the bottle on its side. The roaches can squeeze the water out of the cotton when they need it.)

For experiments that need space, a glass fish tank is good. It must have a tight screen cover. A band of Vaseline about an inch wide just below the inside top edge of the tank will help to keep the roaches in.

Build Your Own Ant Maze

■ By running some ants through a maze, you will discover many interesting things about them—their feeding habits, the way they meet each other, how they find their way about. This chapter tells how to collect some ants, how to set up a maze, and how to study the ways of ants. The maze and nest jar are shown on the next page; directions for making them are on page 84.

How to Collect Ants for Your Maze

When you collect your ants, take a spade, a large spoon, and the nest jar, using an extra lid without holes in it. Two kinds of ants that you can easily find for your maze are (1) the medium-sized black ants that nest in lawns, in gardens, and under rocks in fields, and (2) the gray field ants that often nest under stones.

When you find a nest, dig up the clump of earth containing the opening. Look for the ants' tunnel beneath it. Dig along the tunnel carefully, examining each spadeful for chambers of the nest. Scoop up the ants, their cocoons, and the pale, grub-like larvae, and drop them in your nest jar. If you dig far enough, you may capture the queen. She will be considerably larger than the workers around her. Try to get the queen. Without her, your ants will die sooner than they would normally.

After you get your ants home, connect the nest jar with the maze, drop water in the moisture tube, and cover the jar. By keeping out the light you will encourage the ants to build tunnels next to the glass where you will be able to see them. Leave the ants alone for a day or so to get used to their surroundings. Then try some investigations.

How to Observe Your Ants

Put your ants on a regular feeding schedule. This is important. Mix a

smooth board 6 inches wide, 2 feet long
feet of wooden molding ½ inch square
feet of felt weather stripping ½ inch wide
block of wood 2 inches square, ½ inch thick
glass tubes, each about a foot long
feet of flexible plastic tubing that you can see through. The glass and flexible tubing must have openings at least ¼ of an inch across.
large wide-mouthed glass jar with a screw-on cover. A 2-quart mayonnaise jar will do.
pieces of window glass 4 inches square
china cement
a small saw
a pair of sharp scissors
adhesive tape

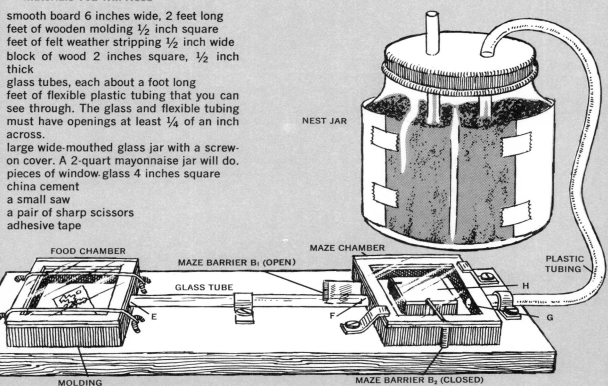

NEST JAR

FOOD CHAMBER

MAZE BARRIER B₁ (OPEN)

GLASS TUBE

MAZE CHAMBER

PLASTIC TUBING

E

F

H

G

MOLDING

MAZE BARRIER B₂ (CLOSED)

half teaspoonful of sugar in half a cup of water and store it in a clean bottle. Feed your ants at the same hour every day by using a clean medicine dropper and putting four or five drops of sugar water on a piece of cardboard. Place the piece of cardboard in the feeding chamber. (At this stage, both maze barriers should be left in the open position.) After a while the ants will find their way from the nest into the plastic tube, through the maze, and into the feeding chamber.

Starting half an hour before feeding time, keep a record of where the ants are moving. Every ten minutes during the half-hour, count the number of ants in the feeding chamber. If no ants are in it, enter 0 in your record. After the ants have learned to find their way into the feeding chamber, count the number of ants in the chamber every 10 minutes after feeding time for half an hour, and keep a record of the totals.

Do this exactly the same way for several days. Use a piece of clean cardboard each time you feed them. Be sure the light always shines on the maze and feeding chamber from the same side.

Get a magnifying glass and watch the ants closely. What does an ant do when it finds food? What do the ants do when they meet each other? Do most of them follow one pathway through the maze? How long does it take most of the ants to learn when it is feeding time?

After the ants are used to the trip to the feeding chamber, make a dead end in the maze by sliding the maze barrier B₁ into the passageway to block it off. The barrier must fit snugly in its groove and against the center

83

block (H) so the ants cannot get past. What do the ants do when they come to it? How soon do they find the other way through the maze? How long does it take before most of the ants have learned to bypass the dead end?

When the ants have learned to avoid the barrier, open it again and close barrier B_2. How long does it take them to find the new pathway to the food?

Change the ants' food from time to time. Double the amount of sugar in the mixture. Cut it in half. Try different kinds of food. How do these changes affect the ants? Shift the light from one side of the maze to the other. Does this affect the ants? How?

Not all these things are easy to do, and you may have to try more than once until you succeed. But you will find that the joy of running tests with your own ant colony is worth all the work ■

—*Paul Showers*

HOW TO BUILD THE MAZE AND NEST JAR

Cut the molding into strips $3\frac{1}{2}$ inches long. With it build two 3-inch fences near the ends of the board, overlapping the ends of the strips. Cement the molding in place. With a small saw cut gates in the fences at (E) and (F) just wide enough so that the ends of a glass tube fit into them snugly. Cut a gate at (G) just wide enough for the flexible tubing. Place the 2-inch-square wooden block (H) exactly in the center of the right-hand fence and cement it down. This fence now has a passageway all around the inside. It is the maze chamber.

To make the maze barriers, cut a slit the width of the saw blade at B_1 and another at B_2. Now cut out two strips of cardboard in such a way that they slide snugly back and forth in slits B_1 and B_2. The diagram shows the B_2 barrier in the closed position blocking off the passage; the B_1 barrier is shown open. The fence at the other end of the board is the feeding chamber.

Now connect gates (E) and (F) with a glass tube, fitting the ends into the openings. Fit one end of the flexible tubing in gate (G). For tight fits, you can twist rubber bands around the ends of the tube and tubing, or fasten adhesive tape around the ends. Fasten both to the board with strips of tape (or use metal strips and screws as shown in the diagram). Cut some weather stripping into pieces $3\frac{1}{2}$ inches long and with china cement fix them around the top of the maze and feeding chambers. Cover the gateways with the strips, allowing the cement to run down around the ends of the tubing to fill the chinks. Make sure the cement does not clog the tube openings. Cement a weather strip covering on the top of block (H). When the cement is dry, cover the maze and feeding chambers with squares of glass, holding them in place with strips of adhesive tape (or metal). Another way to hold down the glass tops is to stretch rubber bands between screwed hooks (see diagram).

Your ants will need a nest to live in. Fill about half of the large glass jar with earth. Make two holes in the lid. Push the flexible tube from the maze through one hole until part of it barely touches the earth. Push a glass tube through the other hole, forcing it well down into the earth. Ants must have moisture, but not too much. Drop water down the glass tube with a medicine dropper so that the earth around the base of the tube is kept damp. Keep the earth moist but not wet. For tight, ant-proof connections, you can twist rubber bands around both tubes just above and below the lid.

*More Animals
Without Backbones*

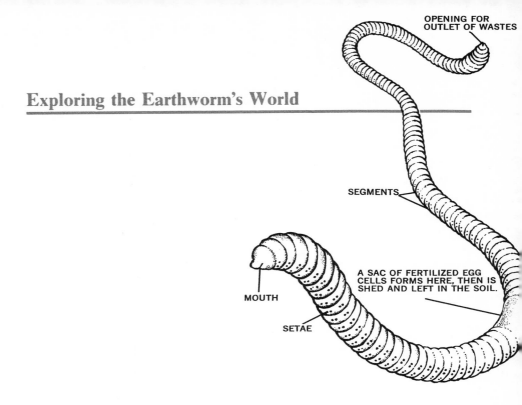

OPENING FOR OUTLET OF WASTES

SEGMENTS

A SAC OF FERTILIZED EGG CELLS FORMS HERE, THEN IS SHED AND LEFT IN THE SOIL.

MOUTH

SETAE

Exploring the Earthworm's World

■ "Ugh!"

Is that the way you feel about earthworms? If so, you should read this chapter just to find out about the lives of these squirmy animals. If, on the other hand, you want to collect and study worms, this chapter will tell you how.

To get and keep a healthy collection of worms, you will need to give them the things they are used to in nature. I will suggest some ways for doing this; you may think of others. To learn about the needs of earthworms, you should observe carefully and take notes as you collect your worms.

Before you collect worms, build a home, or *vivarium* *(see page 88),* for them. Once the vivarium is ready, go on a hunt for worms. Take along a thermometer, an alarm clock, a small scoop or trowel, some small plastic bags, a small plastic bottle of water, and a notebook and pencil. Also get some *litmus paper*. This special paper, available from drug stores, comes in strips of pink or blue. The blue paper turns pink when it is dipped in an acid solution. The pink paper turns blue when it is dipped in a basic, or *alkaline,* solution. You can use litmus paper to find out if earthworms live in acid or basic soil.

Sound the Alarm for Worms

Look for an area covered with dead leaves. Then lift some of the leaves to reach the soil beneath. Put the thermometer on top of the soil, but beneath the leaves. Begin your notes with the date and location and then write down this first temperature reading. Next sink the thermometer about two inches into the soil to find the temperature there. Stand up and take another temperature reading at about your eye level. This way you can mark the reading as taken at your own height. These readings may tell you something about the temperature needs of earthworms.

As you clear away a patch of leaves, stuff a few handfuls of these into a plastic bag. Try to find out what kind of leaves they are. Earthworms "like" some leaves better than others. Biologists have discovered that earthworms are not usually found among oak leaves or pine needles. Mash some leaves in a little water and test this liquid with litmus paper. Are the leaves acid or alkaline?

To actually see some worms, use the alarm clock. Wind the alarm of your clock and set it off. Then press the *face side* against the soil. This is usually a good way of getting whole worms and it allows you to collect worms even in parks where no digging is allowed.

It is not the sound itself that makes the worms leave their tunnels and crawl to the surface. Touch the clock lightly with your fingers while the alarm is ringing. What you feel is what the earthworm feels all over its body. It apparently makes the worm uncomfortable and it tries to get away from that feeling. Do you suppose earthworms can feel your footsteps when you walk on the ground?

Collect about two dozen worms as they come to the surface. Also collect some of their *castings*. These are pellets of soil and plant material that have passed through the bodies of earthworms.

If you look carefully through a magnifying glass at castings, you may find earthworm egg sacs. They are like tiny rubbery "balloons" that are the color of the soil. Actually these balloons hold many eggs. Even if you don't see these, you may later discover you have young worms in your earthworm vivarium.

What Holds a Worm?

After you have collected your worms, dig down in the soil a bit. Investigate the earthworm tunnels. Look for other animals besides worms that live in the same kind of soil. Also look for a worm that is half-out of its burrow. Try to pull it out the rest of the way.

What holds the worm? You can find out by running your fingers down the length of a worm, from head to tail. Next run your fingers the other way, from tail to head. What you feel are bristles that are almost like feet. They're called *setae*.

Look at these with a magnifying glass. Are setae found all around the worm or just on one side? Why?

Somewhere nearby you may find a patch of an entirely different kind of soil. Inspect this for living things, for types of leaves, and for worms, too.

Collect some of this soil in a plastic bag. In your notebook, compare this soil with the soil where you first found earthworms. Write down as many differences as you can discover. Does one kind of soil contain more rocks? Is one more sandy, or more moist? Is it beneath a pine or oak tree? Maybe it is being washed away by the rains, or trampled by feet.

Take out your bottle of water and the litmus paper. Put a few grains of a kind of soil in the bottle cap and mix it with a few drops of water. Test with the litmus paper. Is it acid or alkaline?

In this way, test and collect as many different kinds of soil as you can find. Look for yellowish soil near rocks. Look for hard packed soil along a road. Keep notes on each type and keep the soils in separate plastic bags.

Into the Vivarium

When you get home, count the worms and measure them by counting the number of segments in each. Adult earthworms have 115 to 200 segments; the young have less. Do you have a young population or an old population of worms?

A HOME FOR WORMS

Before you go collecting worms, build a home (called a *vivarium*) for them. The kind shown in the diagram will allow you to watch your worms at work.

To make a vivarium, all you need is two panes of glass and five strips of wood, plus two wood screws and glue. You can buy glass (12 inches by 14 inches) ready-cut in a hardware store. The wood strips should be no wider or deeper than three-fourths of an inch. Get four strips 12 inches long and one strip 14 inches long.

Begin building by drilling a hole four inches in from each end of the 14-inch strip. Now drill holes of the same size in the center of each of two 12-inch strips. Insert the wood screws through the 12-inch strips into the 14-inch strip as shown in the diagram. This is the base and stand of the vivarium. (You may have to gouge out the wood around the screw holes on the underside so that the heads of the screws rest flat with the base.)

Spread glue (a milk-based kind, such as Elmer's) along the inside edges of one pane of glass. Do not glue the top edge. Hold the glass up against the 14-inch strip and place the 12-inch strips in place. Hold them tightly to the glass for a minute, then fasten them to the glass with masking tape, allowing the glue to dry overnight. Do the same with the second pane of glass and your vivarium is ready.

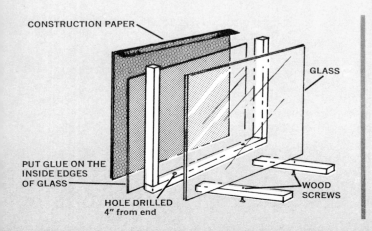

CONSTRUCTION PAPER

GLASS

PUT GLUE ON THE INSIDE EDGES OF GLASS

HOLE DRILLED 4" from end

WOOD SCREWS

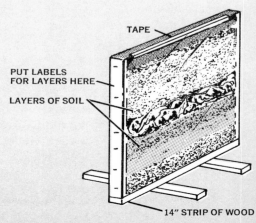

TAPE

PUT LABELS FOR LAYERS HERE

LAYERS OF SOIL

14" STRIP OF WOOD

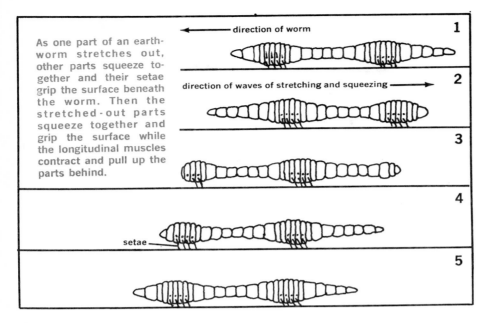

As one part of an earthworm stretches out, other parts squeeze together and their setae grip the surface beneath the worm. Then the stretched-out parts squeeze together and grip the surface while the longitudinal muscles contract and pull up the parts behind.

direction of worm

direction of waves of stretching and squeezing →

setae

1

2

3

4

5

Put the different kinds of soils into the vivarium in layers, making each layer at least an inch deep. Put the "worst" soil (for instance, the hard packed soil from a path) on top. Use leaves as one layer. Mark these layers on the side of the vivarium. This will help you find out what layers the worms choose to live in and whether they mix the layers.

Pour a glassful of water on the top layer of soil and put the worms in the vivarium when all the layers are moist. How long does it take for the water to soak through? Each week you will need to add some more water to keep the layers moist. Note the time it takes each week for the top layer to let the water pass through. Does it always take the same amount of time?

When you add the worms it may appear that they do not like their new home at first. If they knit themselves into a ball on the surface, watch carefully to see what the worms on the bottom of the bundle are doing.

Cover the open top and one side of the vivarium with construction paper. This will give the worms a dark side and a light side.

Although the layers of soil and the layer of leaves provide food, you can offer other foods as well. Occasionally put in some lettuce, cabbage, celery leaves, carrot scrapings, or even bits of hamburger. Put these in the same corner of the vivarium every time. After two weeks or so, shift the food to the other corner. Do the worms find them as quickly?

As you watch your worms day by day, try to find out how they make castings. How do they move through the soil? How do they eat? Watch the mouth of the worm as it works against the glass, searching for food.

Keep your earthworms healthy by providing them with food and moisture. Also try to keep the vivarium at the temperature you found when you explored the earthworm's world ■
                                                                —*Marlene Robinson*

Teach a Worm to Turn

■ If you have been taking good care of your earthworms in their vivarium, you can now try some investigations with them. You may wonder how a worm hears, tastes, and feels, since it has no eyes, ears, or tongue. For example, how did the worms find their food when you changed their feeding place?

An earthworm is sensitive to many things. It reacts to the moisture around it. It reacts to some textures beneath it, and to vibrations. It reacts to light and to chemicals.

To discover where a worm's sensitive areas are, chip a piece of ice so that you can use a small tip like a pointer. With the ice, touch a worm in various places like this: At the head end on the top side, then on the underside . . . in the middle along the top side, then on the underside . . . at the tail end on the top side, then on the underside. What part of the worm's body seems most sensitive? What part is least sensitive?

The area that is most sensitive will be the area where there are the most nerve branchings. Every segment has at least one pair of nerves, but the number of branchings differ.

The cold ice causes some kind of pain and the nerve sends a message— "move"—to the muscles. Those segments that are touched move. But that is not all. The nerves connect with a main nerve cord that is a little like your own spinal cord. The message travels into and along this cord, both toward the brain and the tail end of the worm.

Every segment gets every message! Is it any wonder the whole worm turns? Sometimes it jack-knifes violently. Sometimes it just wriggles away.

90

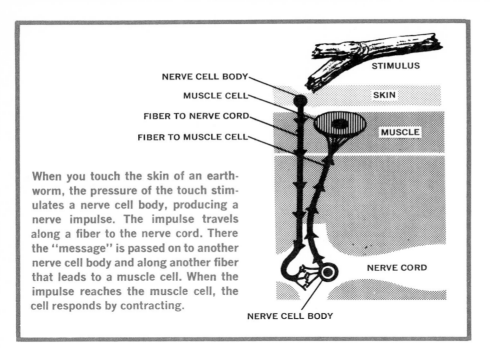

NERVE CELL BODY
MUSCLE CELL
FIBER TO NERVE CORD
FIBER TO MUSCLE CELL

STIMULUS
SKIN
MUSCLE
NERVE CORD

When you touch the skin of an earthworm, the pressure of the touch stimulates a nerve cell body, producing a nerve impulse. The impulse travels along a fiber to the nerve cord. There the "message" is passed on to another nerve cell body and along another fiber that leads to a muscle cell. When the impulse reaches the muscle cell, the cell responds by contracting.

NERVE CELL BODY

The longer you keep poking at the worm the more violent the reaction will become, even in the less sensitive areas. It is like making ripple waves in a pond with one pebble after another.

A worm in this condition is really a "bundle of nerves." It is exhausted. Put this worm into the cool, dark shelter of its vivarium to rest and work with another one for a while. Change worms each time you see these signs of exhaustion.

You might call this "over-reacting" and usually you will want to avoid it. In some of the investigations at the end of this chapter, however, you can use this to discover some fascinating things about the highly sensitive nervous system of the earthworm.

A Worm Can Learn

In 1912 a scientist named Dr. R. M. Yerkes discovered that earthworms will eventually avoid a place where they get a mild electric shock. This

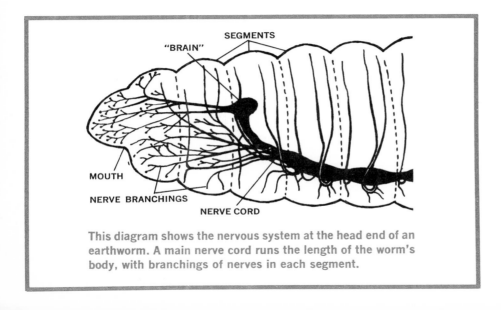

SEGMENTS
"BRAIN"
MOUTH
NERVE BRANCHINGS
NERVE CORD

This diagram shows the nervous system at the head end of an earthworm. A main nerve cord runs the length of the worm's body, with branchings of nerves in each segment.

clearly showed that earthworms can remember things. The worm can also change its actions according to what it remembers. This is called *learning*.

Dr. Yerkes developed a simple way of studying the learning process in worms. It is the T-maze, named for its shape. The worm crawls down the tunnel formed by the base of the T and has a choice of going either right or left at the arms of the T. One choice offered is "agreeable" to the worm; the other choice is not agreeable. Each time the worm goes through the maze and makes a choice, this is called one *trial*. Dr. Yerkes found it took quite a number of trials before a worm could remember which way to turn.

Later, Dr. L. Heck repeated the Yerkes experiment and found that many worms learned the path after 150 trials. One worm made only four "errors" in 120 trials.

The diagram shows how to make a T-maze like those of Drs. Heck and Yerkes. You can use a simple maze to see how fast your worms learn by repeating the same experiment over and over. Remember to allow the worm to rest at least 10 to 15 minutes between trials.

The diagram shows two different ways for making a T-maze. Model A is easier to put together, but Model B will last longer.

Use a plastic or pressed paper tray as a base for Model A. You will find this kind of tray beneath the meat that you can buy in a supermarket. Build the walls of the T out of modeling clay supported, if necessary, with toothpicks. The walls should be at least three inches high. Keep the insides of

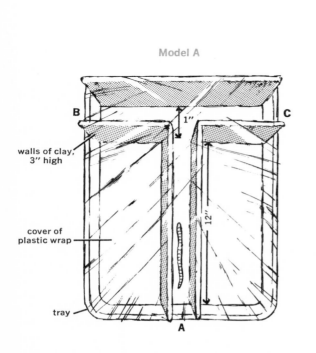

Model A

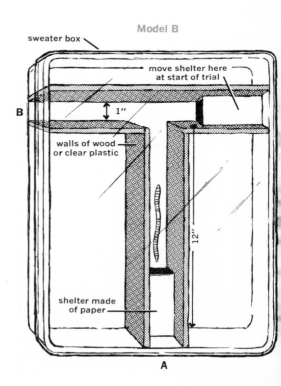

Model B

the walls smooth. Use clear plastic wrap over the whole thing as a "lid." Punch a few air holes in the plastic.

Model B can be constructed *inside* a clear plastic sweater box. These come with lids, and the walls should just barely touch the lid when it is in place. You can make the walls from strips of hard plastic or any smooth wood. Glue the walls into place.

All the walls in both models should be 12 inches long. The corridor along which the worm will crawl should be an inch wide. Label the openings A, B, and C, and keep notes on a worm's choices.

The arms of the T-maze (B and C) will always be exits containing the worm's two "choices." The entrance to the maze is labeled A. The first four inches of A should be a dark shelter where the worm can rest before each trial. To make this shelter, fold an 8½-by-11-inch sheet of paper in half. Then fold this 5½-by-8½-inch paper in half again. Lay a one-inch wide ruler down the center. There will be something like a three-fourths of an inch margin on either side of the ruler. Fold these up against the ruler. Cut off the four inches needed, turn it over and set it inside the maze at A.

When you want to begin a trial, simply remove this little shelter and place it at C. The light will make the worm begin to move down the corridor. You can use a watch or clock with a second hand to time each trial. Begin timing as you lift the paper shelter and end timing when the worm has found the shelter again at C. Keep notes of the number of each trial and the time it takes.

Once your maze and shelter are finished, and you have a notebook, pencil, and watch ready, you can begin to find out how your earthworms learn ■

—*Marlene Robinson*

INVESTIGATIONS

1 . . . Put a worm beneath the shelter at A. Soak a 3-inch by 1-inch piece of blotter in vinegar mixed with water. Put the blotter at the exit end of B, then lift the shelter off the worm at A and put the shelter at C. Does the worm seem to "smell" the vinegar and react before actually touching the blotter? Does the worm react strongly to the vinegar and water solution?

Repeat this experiment using straight vinegar on another piece of blotter. Can the worm tell the difference between a mild acid and a stronger one? Repeat the experiment using a salt solution (1 ounce of salt to 3 ounces of water). You might also repeat the experiment by using "pine needle water" (mash up several ounces of pine needles in water; then soak a piece of blotter in this water).

(Continued on the next page)

2 . . . Clear the insulation off the last inch of the wires attached to a dry cell. Set these across the corridor at B. Then start a worm out at A and put the shelter at C, as before. When the worm crawls across both wires the circuit is completed and the worm gets a mild electric shock. This is something like the vibration of an alarm clock that can be used to bring worms to the surface of the soil. Do your worms seem more sensitive to chemicals or to vibrations?

3 . . . Just how sensitive is the earthworm's skin? You probably know the story about the princess who could feel a pea buried beneath a dozen mattresses. We would not quite expect the same of the earthworm, but do you suppose it can tell the difference between sandpaper and cotton? Put a 1-inch by 3-inch piece of sandpaper at exit B. Instead of the shelter, spread cotton along the end of exit C. On another trial, put sand at exit B and garden soil at exit C.

4 . . . Make a cone with a circle of paper. Fit the cone to your flashlight and tape it in place. Snip a small hole in the end of the cone. This narrows the beam of light so that you can shine it on a small part of the worm. Shine the beam of light on a worm when it reaches exit B. Aim at the head of the worm. Compare the reactions with those in investigations 1 and 2.

5 . . . What temperature changes can a worm feel? Fill the end of exit B with crushed ice. Put the shelter at C. Will the worm crawl onto the ice at all? What happens if you block exit C and put the shelter beyond the ice at B? Will the worm crawl over the ice to get to the shelter?

The following investigations are a different kind. Do not use the "rest period" with the following.

6 . . . Soak a worm in a glass of water for 20 minutes, then repeat Investigation 1. Does a nearly drowned worm react to chemicals as fast as a rested, normal one? Try drying out a worm by leaving it on the table top uncovered for 20 minutes and then repeat Investigation 1.

7 . . . Expose a worm to bright light for 20 minutes. Do not let it dry out (keep it in a dish with a few drops of water). Then repeat Investigation 3. Does the worm exposed to bright light behave the same as a worm that rested in the dark shelter?

8 . . . Chill a worm in the refrigerator for 10 minutes before repeating Investigation 5. Later wrap the worm in damp cotton and place it near a radiator where it can warm up. Then repeat Investigation 5. Does a worm move faster when it is warm or cold?

Do you find that the worms act the same in Investigations 6, 7, and 8 as they did in Investigations 1–5? Would you say that the way a worm acts has a lot to do with what has happened to it before a trial?

Raise Your Own Brine Shrimp

■ What kind of pet do you have? A cat? A dog? Perhaps some tropical fish? How would you like to have about 100 more pet animals? You can watch these pets as they hatch from eggs and grow right before your eyes.

To get some of these animals, go to a pet shop or aquarium supply store. Ask for a small bottle of *brine shrimp* eggs. Brine shrimp are small relatives of lobsters and crabs. Full-grown adults are only about a third of an inch long. By watching them through a hand lens or microscope, you can learn a lot about the lives of these fascinating animals.

You can buy hundreds of brine shrimp eggs for about 50 cents. Be sure to ask for plain eggs, not bottles of eggs with salt and food included. Once you have the eggs, you can start raising your 100 pets.

Setting Up Your Shrimp Hatchery

Start your investigation into the life of the brine shrimp by sprinkling a few of the eggs on a sheet of white paper. Look at them with a hand lens. Or put them on a microscope slide and look at them under a low-power microscope lens. The eggs look like tiny balls with a dent in one side. What color are they? Measure the eggs now and later on to see how they change in size (*see "Measuring with a Microscope," on page 59*).

To raise brine shrimp, first fill a wide-mouthed quart jar or a bowl with water. Use water from a stream or pond if possible. If the water is from a faucet, let it stand about 24 hours to let the chlorine in the water escape into

95

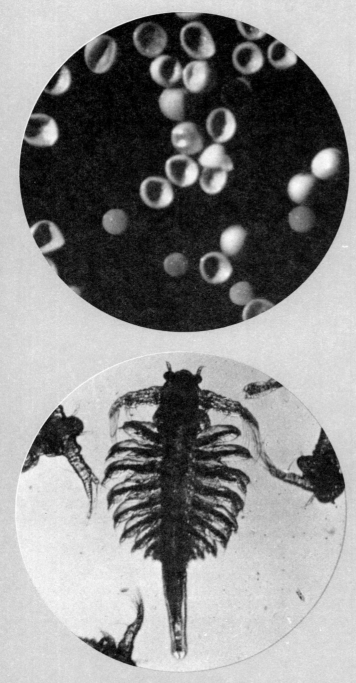

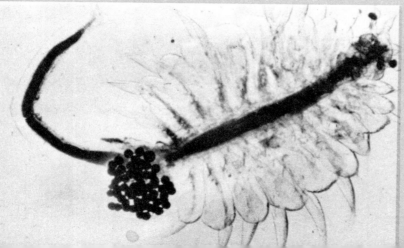

This photo taken through a microscope shows a female brine shrimp with a cluster of eggs within her body. You may be able to keep brine shrimp until they produce eggs.

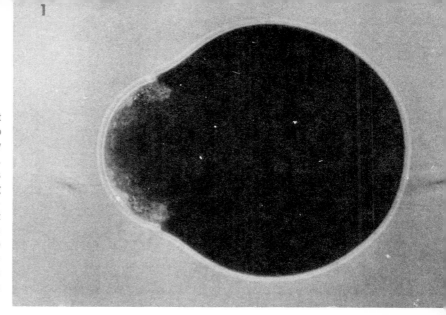

After a few hours in salt water, a brine shrimp begins forcing its way out of its egg (photo 1). As it squirms free, it is enclosed in a covering that partly hides its antennae and eye spot (photo 2). The shrimp's antennae (photo 3) help it break free of its covering and are used as oars until the animal's legs develop.

ANTENNA

EYE SPOT

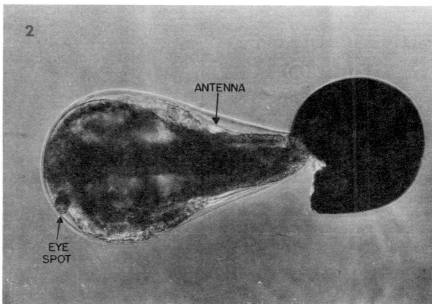

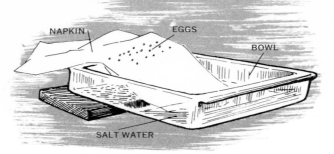

NAPKIN   EGGS   BOWL

SALT WATER

the air. Then dissolve two teaspoonfuls of salt in the water. Use *non-iodized* salt (if iodine has been added, the label on the saltbox will say so). You can also use *sea salt,* which you can buy at a drug store.

Now put about 20 brine shrimp eggs in the water and put the container where sunlight will reach it. Try to keep the temperature of the water between 70 and 80 degrees F.

While you are hatching eggs in this way, you can start some more eggs on a piece of absorbent paper, such as a paper napkin. Put the napkin on the bottom of a bowl and tip the bowl slightly. Add salt water to the bowl until one end of the napkin is covered by the salt water (*see diagram*). Water will move through the paper until the whole napkin is wet. Sprinkle a few eggs on the damp paper (not in the water).

Hatching eggs in this way makes it easier for you to watch the shrimp hatch. Use a hand lens or, if you want a really close look, tear off a piece of the damp paper that holds some eggs and put the paper on a microscope slide. For the best view, use *top lighting*—put a piece of black paper under the slide and have strong light shining on the top of the microscope stage.

Examine some of the eggs after they have been in the water (or on the damp napkin) for about an hour. What effect does the water seem to have on the eggs? Does water just soften the eggs, or is some of the water taken into the eggs? Have the eggs changed in size or shape?

Watching Shrimp Hatch

Some of the eggs may start to split open six to eight hours after they are placed in the salt water. You may see a shrimp forcing its way through the crack in the egg. At this stage, the shrimp is called a *nauplius.* If you look at an egg at this stage under the low-power microscope lens, you will notice that the nauplius is enclosed in a thin, clear covering.

After a few more hours, the pear-shaped nauplius squirms free of the egg, but it is still wrapped in the covering. If you look closely, you should see a red "eye spot," as well as the beginnings of "legs." These "legs" are really *antennae;* later on the shrimp will develop 11 pairs of real legs. The motion of these antennae helps the shrimp to breathe. It also helps it to break out of its clear covering. The shrimp will probably escape from its covering between 18 and 24 hours after the egg was put into the water. Then the shrimp's three pairs of antennae serve as oars to move the animal quickly about in its salt water swimming pool.

To get a better look at a shrimp, slow it down by draining its swimming pool. First, pick it up with a medicine dropper. Do this by squeezing the

98

rubber bulb of the dropper as you bring the dropper's open end near a shrimp. Then stop squeezing the bulb and the shrimp will be sucked into the dropper along with some water.

Squeeze the shrimp and some water onto a microscope slide, and soak up some of the water with a bit of napkin. Now the brine shrimp is free enough to wiggle but not to swim. You should be able to see it clearly with a hand lens or low-power microscope lens. How big is it?

Brine shrimp are especially interesting to watch for the first few days after hatching. They shed their skins two or three times as they grow. You may even be able to keep them alive until they produce more eggs. Keep only about 10 shrimp to a quart of water. Remove the extras by picking them up with a medicine dropper and putting them in another container. For food, put about one grain of dried yeast in the container each day. (You can also use your extra shrimp as food for fish and other aquarium animals.) ■
—Raymond E. Barrett

INVESTIGATIONS

Some animals are attracted to light. Others turn away from light. How would you test the reaction of brine shrimp to light?

Try putting about 10 or 20 brine shrimp eggs in several different kinds of water. Do you think that the eggs will hatch in *fresh* water? In water that has *iodized* salt in it? Also put the same number of eggs in water with half a teaspoon of salt, or with two *tablespoons* of salt. You may think of some other mixtures. Keep all of the solutions at the same temperature.

Do all of the eggs hatch? In which solution do the greatest number hatch? Do they hatch more slowly in some solutions than in others?

Do you think brine shrimp would hatch in the dark? Or in cold water? Must they have air to hatch? To find out, set up six containers with two teaspoonfuls of salt (or sea salt), dissolved in a quart of water. Put about 20 eggs in each one. Then number the jars 1 through 6. Put jar 1 in a warm, light place. Put jar 2 beside it, but carefully pour salad oil on top of the water to shut out the air.

Put the next two jars beside the others, covering the surface of one with salad oil. Then cover both of them with black construction paper to keep light from the eggs. Finally, cover jar 5 with black paper and put it in a refrigerator. Pour salad oil on the surface of jar 6, cover it with black paper, and put it in the refrigerator too.

Check the jars every day for about two weeks. Which one seems best for hatching eggs? In which container do the eggs hatch first? Do they hatch in all of them?

Compare the containers that were warm with those that were cold. Does temperature seem to make any difference in hatching of eggs? Compare those in darkness with those in light. Is light needed for the eggs to hatch? Also compare those containers that were exposed to air with those that had oil on top of the water. Do the eggs need air to hatch? Did all of the shrimp that hatched stay alive the same length of time?

| 1 WARM LIGHT AIR | 2 WARM LIGHT NO AIR | 3 WARM DARK AIR | 4 WARM DARK NO AIR | 5 COLD DARK AIR | 6 COLD DARK NO AIR |

*The Ways of
Small Mammals*

Into a Gerbil's World

■ What animal looks like a furry mouse, is very curious, and can be more fun than a monkey? If you haven't guessed, it is a *gerbil* (pronounced JUR-bil). These little mammals make excellent pets. They are clean and quiet. Perhaps you can buy one or two for pets.

Taking Care of Gerbils

The first thing you will need for your gerbil is a cage. A fish tank makes a good cage even if it is cracked. You could also use a bird cage, or make a cage from a wooden box, giving it a wire front.

Your gerbil will escape from its cage if it finds an opening. For this reason, keep the cage inside a bathtub for the first few days. Then if the gerbil does get out, it can't get away. The sides of a tub are too slippery for gerbils to climb.

Gerbils are not fussy eaters. They grow well on a regular diet of bird-seed. Put in a lot of seed so there is always enough for the gerbil to eat. It won't overeat. Give your gerbil some lettuce and carrots, too.

Gerbils come from China, on the edge of the Gobi Desert. Because there is not much water in the desert, gerbils need only a few drops of water each day. Your gerbil won't need to drink any water at all if you provide foods that have water in them. Lettuce, carrots, celery, and grapes contain a lot of water. In the desert gerbils eat the roots, seeds, and leaves of desert plants.

A Shredded Paper "Machine"

If you ever want something shredded, give it to your gerbil. It will tear up almost anything. Put some things in the animal's cage to see if it rips

101

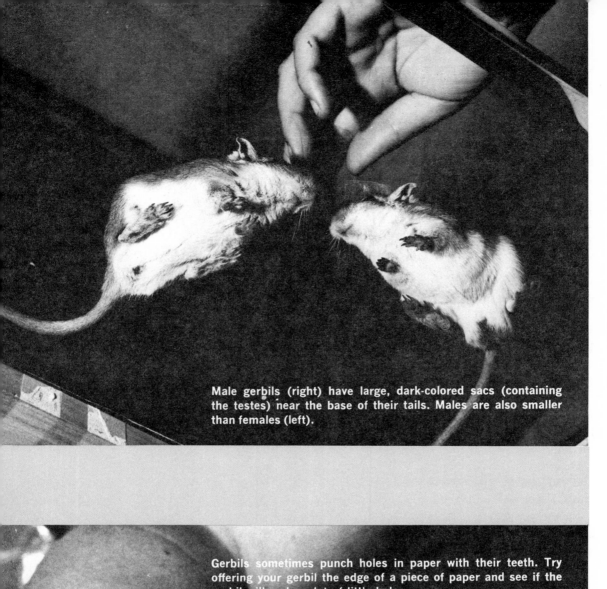

Male gerbils (right) have large, dark-colored sacs (containing the testes) near the base of their tails. Males are also smaller than females (left).

Gerbils sometimes punch holes in paper with their teeth. Try offering your gerbil the edge of a piece of paper and see if the gerbil will make a lot of little holes.

them apart. You might try paper towels, colored paper, old socks, cardboard boxes, and spelling tests. Think of some other things to try.

Watch the gerbil as it works. What teeth does it use to shred paper? How does it hold the paper while chewing? Does your gerbil ever tear up things at night in the dark? Does it use some of the shredded paper or cloth to make a fluffy bed?

Gerbils gnaw for hours on cardboard, plastic, and even wire. This doesn't mean they are trying to escape or to get something to eat. They need to gnaw. Like other rodents, gerbils have front teeth that never stop growing. Gnawing wears away the teeth so they keep at the right length.

If you use a fish tank for a cage you can see how gerbils dig tunnels. In the desert gerbils build tunnels in the sand, where they hide from other animals.

Pack about 10 inches of clean soil into the fish tank. Mix water with the soil until it is damp. If the soil becomes too dry, the gerbil's tunnels will fall in, so sprinkle some water on top every day.

Put in your gerbil and see if it starts to dig. Does the gerbil dig with its front feet, like a dog? Does it take a long time to make a tunnel?

Sometimes gerbils dig tunnels right next to the glass. Then you can look in and see what they do underground. A gerbil is more likely to dig near the glass if you cover the glass with a piece of dark paper. Take the paper off only when you want to see inside.

Gerbils need exciting places to explore. They spend hours crawling in and out of cardboard tubes. Give your gerbil a tube from the inside of a paper towel roll. Watch to see what the gerbil does with it.

Maybe you can make a little ladder or sliding board for your gerbil. Gerbils are good climbers and acrobats. They soon become skillful with rear and front claws.

Watch a Gerbil Family

If you have two gerbils, and one is a male and the other a female, you may be lucky enough to get some young. A mother gerbil usually has four

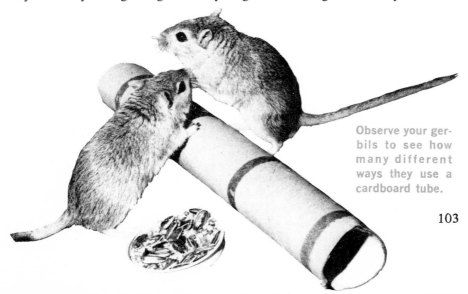

Observe your gerbils to see how many different ways they use a cardboard tube.

103

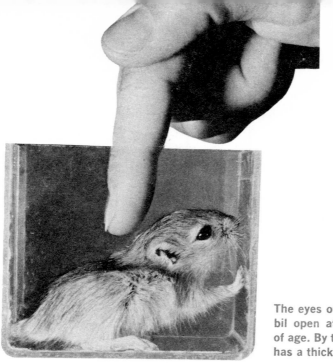

The eyes of a young gerbil open at three weeks of age. By then the gerbil has a thick coat of fur.

or five young at a time. Sometimes, though, a gerbil family has as many as 10 young.

The best way for you to care for young gerbils is to leave them alone. Their mother knows what to do. She feeds and washes them, and keeps them warm in her nest. You can help her only by supplying plenty of food and nest-making material.

At first the new gerbils are very tiny. Their eyes are sealed shut and they have no fur. In a few days they grow their first coat of light brown fur. All they do is wiggle around and make faint *cheeps.*

When the young gerbils are two weeks old, they will have begun walking around the cage. Often they bump into things, because their eyes are still unopened. After three weeks their eyes open. They will soon eat regular gerbil food, instead of drinking their mother's milk. The young gerbils now can be taken away from their mother and put into a home of their own. In three months they will be full-grown adult gerbils ■

—*David Webster*

INVESTIGATION

What do you think your gerbil likes to eat for a special treat? What would it like best, a dandelion flower, a piece of candy, some ice cream? You can find out by putting three or four foods that you want to test in the gerbil's cage. The food should be in separate dishes so you can tell how much of each one has been eaten. Look in the dishes the next morning. How much of each food was eaten? Which of the foods tested does the gerbil seem to like best?

You can keep trying different foods to find out what the gerbil likes best of all. Does your gerbil prefer corn flakes, dog biscuits, a cactus, toast, popcorn, grapes, or cheese?

If you have more gerbils than you want, give them to a friend or someone else who will give them good care. *Do not let them go.* If you let gerbils go outdoors, they will probably die. If they survive, they could become a serious nuisance.

How to Train a Mouse

■When you watch circus animals perform, you generally see only the last stage of a training process. If you could watch an animal being trained, you would see that its training takes place step by step. Even the most spectacular animal act is made up of a series of single steps.

Psychologists who work with animals have discovered that there are several basic methods by which we can teach animals.

You can use one of these methods and train animals yourself. This chapter explains how to build a special cage for training laboratory mammals such as mice and rats. It also tells how to carry out the first training steps. (The chapters that follow explain more advanced techniques.) Large mammals, such as whales, pigs, or lions, as well as dogs, cats, and horses, have been trained to perform amazing feats. With patience and cleverness you can train small mammals as well as larger ones.

How To Set Up the Cage

A wire mesh cage is suitable for training a mouse, rat, gerbil, or hamster. It can be used both for the animal's home and for its training. You can also use it for investigations in later chapters.

If everything goes well, the animal never needs to be removed from its cage. Cleaning the cage and feeding can be done from the outside. You can tie the door firmly shut, a fact that may comfort your family! Having used only metal material to make the cage, you need not worry about odors. It is usually urine that has soaked into wooden parts of cages that makes the worst odors. Wire mesh cages are practically self-cleaning.

Put several layers of newspaper in a cut-down cardboard box and set the cage in it. Cut the walls of the box so that they are about as high as the wire cage. This will protect the animal from drafts. All droppings and urine will fall through the floor of the cage on to the newspaper. Replace the newspaper under the cage every day to assure cleanliness.

Avoid open water containers. A water bottle that lets the animal get water by licking the end of a tube can be bought at most pet or dime stores. Tie this bottle to the outside of the cage so that the tube reaches into the cage. Water should always be available.

First Steps in Training Your Animal

You can buy a mouse or a small rat at a pet store. These mammals are sensitive to cold. Be especially careful to protect them from drafts. At first the animal may be very shy and stay at one corner of the cage. Let it

INVESTIGATIONS

Do some mice learn faster than others? Do young mice learn faster or slower than older mice that have the same inherited characteristics? Do you think that some mice are born with the ability to learn faster than others? Here are some ways to investigate these questions. You will need enough cages to keep each mouse in its own cage. If you treat the mice exactly alike, you can compare how fast the different ones learn.

1 . . . Compare several mice to see how long each takes to learn to come to the dish when food is dropped in. Keep a record of your findings on a chart like this:

	Mouse Number					
	1	2	3	4	5	6
Number of days to condition to the sound of food dropping						

2 . . . If you live near a college that uses mice in its laboratories, one of the professors may have extra pure-bred mice (with the same inherited characteristics) that he can give you. Try to get two batches of mice of different ages, say some that are two months old and some that are six months old. Compare the learning speeds of the young mice and the older mice from the same pure-bred parents and record your findings on a chart for each batch.

get used to eating from the food container. This may take several days. Drop a little bit of food into the tube and walk away. Return occasionally, and if the previous food has been eaten, drop in some more food. As the days go by, the animal will come to the food cup more and more readily. If it is hungry it may already be waiting at the food cup or it may run to the cup when it hears you coming.

Your animal must be hungry when you train it. Cut some hard cheese into very small cubes about half the size of a grain of rice. Small pieces are important. Using them, you can feed your animal several times without dulling its appetite. Thus you can give your animal more training trials at any one training session.

Mice and rats work best and learn fastest when they have been without food for about 10–20 hours, depending on their age. Try a 10-hour hunger period first. After it has eaten from the food container for several days, the animal should approach the container when you come up to the cage. If it does not, increase the hunger period to 15 or if necessary to 20 hours for older animals. Small mammals need food often. Feed your mice daily after

HOW TO MAKE A CAGE FOR SMALL MAMMALS

ll need a 38-by-24-inch piece of galvanized half-inch wire mesh (called re cloth), which you can buy at most hardware stores. Use a pair of to cut the wire mesh and bend the large piece of wire mesh as shown iagram to form the legs, bottom, top and sides of the cage. Fold each two 6-by-12-inch strips in half to make two 6-inch squares two layers ttach one square to one end of the cage by putting short pieces of e through the mesh and twisting the ends together. Use wire in the ay to hinge the other square to one side of the cage at the other end, lock this door closed at the other side of the cage. You can also use make the legs firm.

e the feeder, get a metal lid about 1½ to 2 inches in diameter with a nch to ¾ inch high. With hammer and nail, make two small holes about apart and tie the lid to the floor of the cage with wire. Place it next ide of the cage near the door end. The feeding tube should be 8 inches d from ¼ to ½ inch in diameter. You can use a section from a hollow rod, some glass tubing, or make a tube by rolling heavy tin foil. Tie e to the side of the cage so that it sticks up through the top and hangs ½ inch above the metal lid.

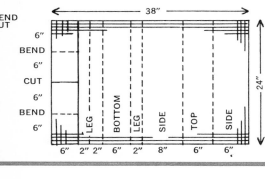

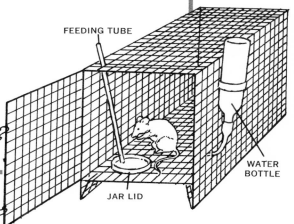

the last training session. Never leave them without water.

Early in the experiment train the animal to come to the food cup as soon as a certain noise is made. For convenience, use the noise which is made by the dropping of the food. You can start this noise or sound training when the animal is close to the food container or when it is actually eating. Wait till the animal is just about to touch a piece of food in the container, then drop one or two more pieces down the feeding tube.

The animal may be frightened from the bang the food makes when it drops. But wait! In a few seconds the animal will come back and eat. Let it eat this time. When the animal reaches for the last piece or when it looks for food in the container, drop some more pieces. Repeat this five to 10 times in one training period. You can have one or two training periods per day, but remember, the animal must be hungry at the beginning of each training period. As the trials are repeated, the animal will startle less and less from the noise. After several days of training it will eat undisturbed from the container while new food bangs into the pan.

Training Reverses a Natural Reaction To Run Away

When you have completed this noise training, you have demonstrated one of the most important steps in animal learning. You have *conditioned,* or accustomed, your animal to the sound of food. At the beginning your animal ran away when the bang occurred. Now it will run toward the container when it hears the very same noise. The sound has become the symbol or cue for food. Psychologists call the sound the *stimulus* for eating.

If the feeding had been soundless you could have tapped on the cage, whistled, or rung a bell just shortly before feeding. This is exactly what the Russian scientist Ivan Pavlov did in some famous experiments early in 1900. He noticed that when dogs smell food, they drool. Saliva flows from their mouths. In his famous "conditioning experiment" he measured the amount of saliva that dogs produce when smelling food. Then he rang a bell just shortly before he gave a dog some food to smell. After repeating this about 20 times, he found that the dog started to drool right after the bell rang. It no longer waited for the odor of food. Pavlov had conditioned the dog to salivate at the sound of the bell alone. He taught the dog a new cue, or stimulus, for salivation.

Your mouse or rat has also learned to react in a new fashion. The noise has become the cue for running *toward* the food container. Can you be sure your animal reacts to the noise alone and not to your hand moving toward the feeder tube, or not to the odor of the cheese? You can make one final test. Cover the cage with cardboard so that the animal can't see your hand moving toward the feeder tube. Take a small piece of stone, instead of food and drop it into the feeder when the animal is away from the food container. Lift the cover to look into the cage. If the animal comes toward the food container now, you can be sure it responds to the noise alone ■

—*Frank Wesley*

108

■ The chapter "How to Train a Mouse" tells how to teach a small mammal to react to the noise of falling food. That type of learning is the simplest kind of learning.

You can also see this sort of learning in humans, especially in babies. Babies cry when they are hungry. They usually stop as soon as they are given a bottle.

Babies get used to hearing certain noises just before they get their bottles —the thump of the refrigerator door, the sound of a faucet, and footsteps. These noises become signals telling the baby that milk is on the way. First the infant will learn to be quiet when it hears the footsteps that come just before the feeding. In another week or so the infant will be quiet as soon as the faucet is turned on to warm up the milk. The faucet noise becomes a cue for footsteps. Cues pick up cues. Humans and other animals form chains of such cues. Dogs and birds have been trained to react to cues seven steps away from the original one.

Now that you know about this simple type of learning you can start experimenting with a more complicated type. It is learning in which the animal itself has to do something to get the reward. Let's train a mouse to ring a bell for its dinner.

Closer and Closer to the Loop

If you have not worked with the mouse for some time, it may need some practice to learn again to come to the food cup when food drops in. When your animal comes readily to the food cup on hearing the noise, you can start to teach it to pull a wire-loop to ring the bell for its meal.

Start this training when the mouse is hungry. Place the bell unit on top of the cage, so that the loop hangs down into the cage and is close to the food cup. Drop one piece of food into the food tube, and wait until this food is eaten. Don't give any more food for a while. The mouse will look around the cup for a second piece. During this search the animal is likely to move around. When it is closest to the loop, you must drop in a piece of food *fast*.

After the food is eaten the mouse will tend to go into the same position that it was in when the food dropped. On the next trial you wait again with the feeding until the mouse is even a little closer to the loop than it was before. The animal need not touch the loop during these beginning trials. It is only necessary that it gets a little closer each time, and that you delay the feeding each time until it does. It will take about five trials before your mouse will actually touch the loop with its nose or foreleg.

Once the animal has touched the loop it may not pull hard enough to ring the bell. Continue to play the waiting game. Wait with feeding until the mouse touches or paws the loop again, but a little stronger than before, or until the animal rears or climbs up on the loop. You may need two or three training sessions of about five to 10 trials each before your animal learns to pull the bell vigorously.

It is important to lift the bell unit off the cage as soon as you end a training session, or as soon as you decide to give your animal or yourself a rest. If you leave the pulling wire in the cage while you are away the animal may pull on it. It would not get any food and would *unlearn* very fast. If you remove the bell assembly promptly after each last trial you will find that your animal will start off the next day about where it left off the previous day.

The animal has to do something before it gets the reward. It learned what to do because you rewarded little steps all leading up to the final bell-ringing act. Each step came about through the animal's natural searching motions. During this training each small step brought the animal closer to your training goal. You might like to try more training of this sort to see how smoothly it works.

Back to the Bell . . .

Your mouse has learned to ring the bell when the loop is directly over the food cup. You can now make the problem harder and move the bell unit all the way to the rear of the cage.

If you do this in one big step it may take several hours before your animal may touch the bell at the new location. Instead, hang the bell first about three inches away from the food cup. There will be only a little hesitation, perhaps none at all, before the animal pulls the loop to get food. On the

110

A BELL FOR MICE TO RING

You can make a bell unit as shown in the drawing out of ⅜-inch metal packing bands. Strips of these bands can be found at the shipping department of an appliance store. Bendable sheet metal or aluminum strips can also be used.

With tinsnips cut a piece 10 inches long and bend it into a 2-inch-wide U-shape. Fold each end twice to form a clip which can be attached on to the top of your wire mesh cage. Punch a small hole at top center.

Take another strip of metal band about 3 inches long. Punch three holes through it, one at each end and one at the center. Tie a small, 1-inch bell tightly to one end with wire. You can buy a bell (attached to a mirror or miniature teeter-totter) at the bird-supply counter in a variety or pet store. Thread a piece of wire through the hole at the other end of this metal strip. Make the wire long enough to reach about 4 inches down into the cage and still form a loop inside the cage. Hang the straight metal strip from the U-shaped metal with wire, as shown. Bend each end of this wire around a nail to keep the ends from slipping back through the holes. If the bell and hanging loop are not in balance, tape a small nut or a little extra wire to the lighter end of the metal strip. The loop at the end of the wire should be narrow enough so that you can easily put it through the wire mesh cage.

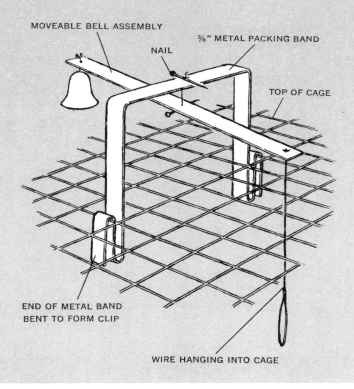

MOVEABLE BELL ASSEMBLY

NAIL

⅜" METAL PACKING BAND

TOP OF CAGE

END OF METAL BAND
BENT TO FORM CLIP

WIRE HANGING INTO CAGE

next day you place the bell six inches more to the rear, on the third day all the way.

Soon the mouse will run to the pulling wire, regardless of its location. It will ring the bell and run to the food cup as soon as food is dropped. Sometimes it will get ahead of itself. It will run before the food is dropped, taking

A boy drops food into the cage to reward his hamster for ringing the bell. Mice can be trained to ring in the same way.

the bell or its own muscular actions as cues. If you refuse to feed it on such occasions it will run right back to the bell and ring some more.

Much of human learning is done this way. In 1920, J. B. Watson, an American psychologist, examined such methods. In a famous experiment, one of his students, Mary Cover Jones, retrained a three-year-old boy who was very much afraid of rabbits. A rabbit was placed into a cage about 20 feet from the boy during the boy's mealtime. At that distance the boy paid little attention to the rabbit and was not bothered by it. A mealtimes, on successive days, the rabbit was brought closer and closer, half a foot or so each day. It took several weeks but finally the rabbit was within the boy's reach and he showed no fear and even played gladly with the rabbit. In this experiment fear was turned into pleasure by exactly the same method you used to teach your mouse to ring for his dinner.

Once your animal has learned to pull the bell, you can demonstrate unlearning. Leave the bell in place but do not feed. Your animal may ring the bell 10 or 20 times before it gives up. Finally it will no longer ring the bell when it wants food. You can leave the bell in place for a whole day to make sure ringing has stopped.

Such "unlearning" can be cancelled out in an interesting way. After the bell has been in the cage for a day and all ringing has stopped, remove the entire bell unit and put it away so that your animal can neither see any part of it nor hear the bell. Keep on feeding your animal without the bell for four or five days. Bring the bell back after that time and put it on the cage when the animal is hungry. Your animal will ring the bell right away. It seems that during the days without the bell the mouse *forgets the forgetting*.

Partial Reward

Train another mouse to ring the bell, just as you did with the first animal. After it has learned to pull the wire, reward it only every second or third time that it rings the bell. The training will not take much longer. But when you try to *stop* the pulling response with this animal, it will take much longer.

This animal may continue for 100 trials before giving up. Animals which get rewards every time will give up much sooner. Pigeons have been trained to peck at a disk 6,000 times per hour, earning food only on five or six of these pecks. In many situations infrequent rewards are much better than steady ones ■   —*Frank Wesley*

Mouse in a Puzzle Box

■ Do you try to solve puzzles for the fun of working on them or for the satis-faction you get from solving them? In either case, the fun or satisfaction you get is a reward for your work. You can help a mouse learn how to solve a puzzle, but the mouse probably won't get much "fun" or "satisfaction" from its work. So you will have to give it some other kind of reward. If the reward is food, the mouse will probably keep trying until it learns to solve the puzzle.

You can make a "puzzle box" by making some slight changes in the "learning cage" for mice or other small mammals. The puzzle the mouse will have to solve is one of finding the way to open a door through which the mouse can get to some food.

When the puzzle box is ready, let your mouse get used to living in the remodeled cage. The side of the cage with the latch handle in it should be considered the living compartment, and the side the door opens into, the feeding compartment. Leave the door open and let the mouse live in either side for one or two days. During this time, feed the mouse *only* in the feeding compartment.

Beginning the Tests

On the third day when you come to the cage, do not feed the mouse. Put the mouse in the living compartment and latch the door closed. Then

113

HOW TO MAKE A PUZZLE BOX

The learning cage for small mammals can easily be converted into a puzz[le] box like the one shown here.

You will need a six-inch-square piece of half-inch wire mesh (the sam[e] material the cage is made of), to make a partition in the cage. You will al[so] need a cabinet or door hinge, a short bolt and nut, a small strip of she[et] metal, and a fishline sinker or other small weight.

Wire one side of the hinge to the partition so that the other side of [the] hinge swings freely. Then use wire cutters to cut an opening in the partiti[on] a little smaller than the swinging part of the hinge.

Use sheet metal cutters to shape a strip of metal into a latch for the doo[r.] Punch a hole in the round part to let the latch turn freely around the bo[lt.] Position the latch so that its end covers just the top corner of the door. Cut o[ne] crosswire of the mesh to allow the latch handle to swing down just enough [to] free the door. A cardboard washer and a nut on the other side of t[he] partition will hold the bolt and latch in position. Attach a small fishing sink[er] or other weight to the latch handle as shown.

Now put the partition in the cage near the "door" end of the cage a[nd] wire it in place. Attach a rubber band from the swinging part of the hinge [to] the side of the cage so it will pull the door open when the latch is raised. Te[st] your puzzle box to make sure that the door and latch work properly an[d] easily before you put your mouse in the cage.

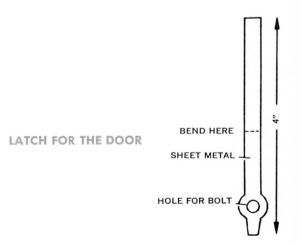

LATCH FOR THE DOOR

BEND HERE

SHEET METAL

HOLE FOR BOLT

4"

DETAILS OF DOOR CONSTRUCTION

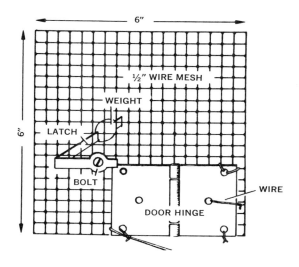

6"

6"

½" WIRE MESH

WEIGHT

LATCH

BOLT

DOOR HINGE

WIRE

COMPLETED PUZZLE BOX

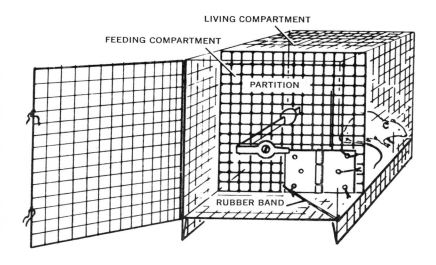

LIVING COMPARTMENT

FEEDING COMPARTMENT

PARTITION

RUBBER BAND

Claire Wesley, the author's daughter, measures the learning speed of a cat in a puzzle box she made from an apple crate. The cat's "reward" is in the dish at the bottom of the picture.

put a small piece of food (a rice or corn flake) on the floor of the feeding compartment near the door. Make a note of the exact time, so you can tell how long it takes for the mouse to open the door.

Not knowing how to open the door, the mouse may try to get at the food by much seemingly useless activity. It may put its nose through the wire at the edge of the door near the food, climb the door, climb on any side of the compartment, including the ceiling. Scientists call such work *random activity,* or *solution by trial and error.* Unless the mouse is very lucky, it may wander around the cage for a few minutes to an hour or so before it presses the lever strongly enough to open the door. Be patient. When the mouse finally opens the door, record the time of the mouse's first trial on a data table like the one in the graph on the next page.

When the mouse has finished eating, put it back into the living compartment and latch the door closed. Put another piece of food in the feeding compartment and immediately begin timing a second trial.

Watch the mouse's activity as you time each trial. See if it spends more time near the door or the latch than in other parts of the living compartment. Does it seem to pull the latch by accident, or "on purpose"? Make notes of your observations on each trial before beginning the next trial.

On the first day, you may run the mouse through five or 10 trials, depending on its patience. When the mouse loses interest in the food, stop the experiment, because the mouse will not try very hard to open the door.

Wait until the next day before running your next set of trials. Compare the two sets of trials. Do you think that the mouse remembered anything it learned the first day?

When Did the Mouse "Learn"?

Whether you have a fast-learning or slow-learning mouse, you will see that the beginning trials take very long. After 10 trials or so, the mouse may

116

press the lever within seconds after you have put the latch back into place. You may not even have enough time to place the food. Your animal may learn to work so fast that it will run back into the living cage as soon as it is through eating.

As the time needed to escape from the living compartment becomes shorter, the mouse's behavior becomes more "streamlined." The mouse spends less and less time in useless activity and goes more directly to its goal, the food. Scientists say the mouse has become *goal-directed*.

On the first trial it looked as if the mouse had no idea what it was supposed to do. After 10 trials or so the animal seemed to be very certain of its actions. Then it seemed to know exactly what to do. When did the mouse learn? When did "trial and error" change into certainty? This question is hard to answer. Perhaps drawing a graph of the data in your table will help you decide when the mouse learned how to open the door.

The graph shows the *learning curve* of a mouse that I tested. It is plotted from the data in the table in the graph. As you can see, each X is straight

This graph shows the learning curve of a mouse whose trial times are recorded in the data table in the corner of the graph. Record the trial times of your mouse in a table like this and plot its learning curve on a graph like this which you can draw on graph paper.

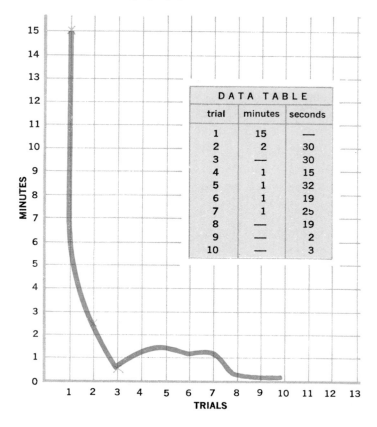

DATA TABLE		
trial	minutes	seconds
1	15	—
2	2	30
3	—	30
4	1	15
5	1	32
6	1	19
7	1	2b
8	—	19
9	—	2
10	—	3

up from the number of the trial it represents and straight to the right of the number of minutes the trial took. The line connecting the X marks is the mouse's learning curve.

This curve shows that my mouse took much longer to complete the first trial than any other trials. (Sometimes the second and third trials may also take a long time.) After the beginning trial, the time decreased rapidly. But then it went up and down a few times, suggesting one of two things: 1) The mouse may have pulled the latch by accident at times, shortening the length of those trials, or 2) It may have learned a little about how to pull the latch, then forgotten a little, taking longer than it took in earlier trials.

PROJECT

Use a graph to plot the learning curve of the mouse you tested. You may have to extend the "minutes" scale upward if the mouse took longer than 15 minutes for any of its trials. From your notes, compare what the mouse was doing during each trial with the direction—up or down—and the height of the curve at that trial. Can you see any connection between the mouse's actions and the length of each trial?

You can see, though, that there was no *one* trial in which the mouse learned to open the door. It learned gradually, but unevenly. It seemed to learn more in the first trials than in the middle ones, and more in the middle trials than in the last ones. When the curve had straightened out, after nine trials, the mouse may have been working as fast as its muscles and nerves could work. This leveled-out part of the curve is called the animal's *physiological limit* by psychologists who study how animals learn.

Who Taught the Mouse?

You may have heard of a device called a "teaching machine." There are many different kinds, but they all do just about the same thing. The machine shows or asks you a question. If you give the correct answer—by pushing the proper button or punching or marking the right place on a paper or card—the machine "rewards" you by asking a more difficult question. If you give the wrong answer, some teaching machines will ask you simpler questions whose answers help you find the correct answer to the question you missed.

The puzzle box is a very simple kind of teaching machine. The "question" it "asks" the mouse is this: How can I get into the feeding compartment to get the food? At first the mouse didn't know what to do, and that probably

118

explains its random activity. But soon after the mouse touched the lever by accident on the first trial, it got the food. On the second and third trials, the mouse probably carried out its random activities closer and closer to the door latch. At this stage, it was hard to tell whether the mouse's actions were accidental, or whether it was staying near the latch on purpose.

After 10 or more trials, the mouse was pulling the latch and opening the door in much less time than the earlier trials took, and taking about the same time for each trial. Scientists say that the more "streamlined" and fast an animal's action becomes, the more we can believe that the animal is acting with a "purpose." We may never be sure about this, because other animals can't tell humans what they "think" or "feel." Nevertheless, other animals can learn successfully.

In this case, you provided the teaching machine and the reward. The mouse taught itself how to solve the puzzle and win the reward ■

—Frank Wesley

INVESTIGATIONS

If you can obtain several mice (or hamsters, gerbils, guinea pigs, or other small mammals), you might test them and plot their learning curves. Are the curves about the same shape for all the mice you test? Are their curves different in shape from those of other mammals?

Can you think of a way to teach yourself how to do something and plot your learning curve for that activity? One way would be to get a small jig-saw puzzle or a "Chinese puzzle" made of pieces of wood that fit together in a special way. Have a friend take it apart and mix up the parts, then have him time your trials in putting the puzzle together again. Plot your learning curve for the puzzle. Can you figure out at what point you learned how to solve the puzzle? (Is completing the puzzle a big enough reward to keep you trying, or do you have to invent a "better" reward?) Can you think of other ways to test your learning ability?

Appendix A

Exploring In Books

The first group of books below includes general books on keeping and studying small animals of many kinds, including mammals. The others are arranged in groups similar to some of the main sections of the book. The simpler books are marked (I) for *Intermediate*; the more difficult books are marked (A) for *Advanced*.

GENERAL

Animals in Field and Laboratory: Science Projects in Animal Behavior, by Seymour Simon, McGraw-Hill Book Company, New York, New York, 1968. (A)

The Curious Gerbils, McGraw-Hill Book Company (Webster Division), Manchester, Missouri, 1967. (I)

Field Book of Nature Activities and Conservation, by William Hillcourt, G. P. Putnam's Sons, New York, New York, 1961. (I)

A Guide to Nature Projects, by Ted Pettit, W. W. Norton & Company, Boston, Massachusetts, 1966. (I)

How to Make a Miniature Zoo, by Vinson Brown, Little, Brown and Company, Boston, Massachusetts, 1957. (I)

How to Raise and Train Gerbils, by D. G. Robinson, Jr., T. F. H. Publications, Inc., Jersey City, New Jersey, 1967. (I)

The Living Laboratory, by James and Rebecca Witherspoon, Doubleday & Company, Inc., Garden City, New York, 1960. (A)

Nature in Miniature, by Richard Headstrom, Alfred A. Knopf, New York, New York, 1968. (A)

Small Pets from Woods and Fields, by Margaret W. Buck, Abingdon Press, New York, New York, 1960. (I)

120

AQUARIUMS AND TERRARIUMS

Adventures with Freshwater Animals, by Richard Headstrom, J. B. Lippincott Company, Philadelphia, Pennsylvania, 1964. (I)

All About Guppies, by L. F. Whitney and Paul Hahnel, T. F. H. Publications, Jersey City, New Jersey, 1964. (A)

Along the Seashore, by Margaret W. Buck, Abingdon Press, New York, New York, 1964. (I)

Aquariums, by Anthony Evans, Dover Publications, Inc., New York, New York, 1952. (A)

The Care of Pet Turtles, by H. G. Dowling and S. Spencook, New York Zoological Society, New York, New York, 1960. (I)

Exotic Aquarium Fishes, by William T. Innes, and edited by George S. Myers, Aquarium Publishing Company, Maywood, New Jersey, 1967. (A)

Field Book of Seashore Life, by Roy W. Miner, G. P. Putnam's Sons, New York, New York, 1950. (A)

Know How to Keep Saltwater Fishes, by William P. Braker, Pet Library, Ltd., New York, New York, 1967. (I)

The New Field Book of Freshwater Life, by Elsie Klots, G. P. Putnam's Sons, New York, New York, 1966. (A)

Reptiles as Pets, by Paul Villiard, Doubleday & Company, Inc., Garden City, New York, 1969. (A)

The Salt Water Aquarium in the Home, by Robert Straughan, A. S. Barnes & Company, New York, New York, 1969. (A)

The Salt Water Aquarium Manual, by Robert J. Valenti, Aquarium Stock Co., New York, New York, 1968. (A)

Salt Water Aquariums, by Barbara and John Waters, Holiday House, New York, New York, 1967. (I)

Seashores, by Herbert Zim and Lester Ingle, Golden Press, New York, New York, 1955. (I)

Turtles, by R. Church, T. F. H. Publications, Jersey City, New Jersey, 1963. (I)

Unusual Aquarium Fishes, by Alan M. Fletcher, J. B. Lippincott Company, Philadelphia, Pennsylvania, 1968. (I)

Your Terrarium, by Mervin Roberts, T. F. H. Publications, Jersey City, New Jersey, 1963. (I)

MICROSCOPES AND THEIR USE

Adventures with Your Microscope, by Richard Headstrom, J. B. Lippincott Company, Philadelphia, Pennsylvania, 1941. (I)

Exploring with Your Microscope, by Julian Corrington, McGraw-Hill Book Company, New York, New York, 1957. (I)

The How and Why Wonder Book of the Microscope and What You See, by Martin Keen, Wonder Books, New York, New York, 1961. (I)

How to Use a Microscope, by W. G. Hartley, The Natural History Press, Garden City, New York, 1964. (A)

Through the Microscope, by M. D. Anderson, The Natural History Press, Garden City, New York, 1965. (A)

Under the Microscope, by Tay Sloan, Children's Press, Chicago, Illinois, 1968. (I)

Water Animals for Your Microscope, by Edward Lindemann, Crowell-Collier Press, New York, New York, 1967. (I)

INSECTS AND OTHER ANIMALS WITHOUT BACKBONES

Adventures with Insects, by Richard Headstrom, J. B. Lippincott Company, Philadelphia, Pennsylvania, 1963. (I)

The Bug Club Book, by Gladys Conklin, Holiday House, New York, New York, 1966. (I)

The Earthworm, by Albert Wolfson and Arnold Ryan, Harper and Row, New York, New York, 1955. (A)

Earthworms, by Dorothy Hogner, Thomas Y. Crowell Company, New York, New York, 1953. (I)

How to Follow the Adventures of Insects, by Vinson Brown, Little, Brown & Company, Boston, Massachusetts, 1968. (I)

Appendix B

BIOLOGICAL SUPPLY HOUSES

When writing to a biological supply house, do not simply ask for a copy of their catalog. In at least one case, the catalog weighs several pounds and may cost the company several dollars. Most dealers prefer to send catalogs to schools, laboratories, and other places from which they are likely to receive large orders. You may be able to borrow a copy of a catalog from a high school biology teacher or college professor.

With or without a catalog, your letter will get best results if you take care to explain fully what you need. The dealer may not carry what you want; he may sell it only in large quantities; or he may have it only during certain seasons. After describing what sort of equipment, animals, or other things you want, ask about cost (including shipping). In the list below, those companies marked with an asterisk (*) sell animals and equipment for salt-water aquariums. This list includes some of the biggest and best-known companies; you may find others listed in the yellow pages of your telephone directory under "scientific apparatus and equipment" and "aquarium supplies."

* **Aquarium Stock Company,** 31 Warren Street, New York, New York 10007
Cambosco Scientific Company, 342 Western Ave., Boston, Massachusetts 02135
Carolina Biological Supply Company, Burlington, North Carolina 27215
Central Scientific Company, 1700 W. Irving Park Road, Chicago, Illinois 60613
* **Coral Reef Exhibits,** P. O. Box 59-2214, Miami, Florida 33159
General Biological Supply Company, 8200 S. Hoyne Avenue, Chicago, Illinois 60620
* **Gulf Specimen Company,** P. O. Box 206, Panacea, Florida 32346
Sherwin Scientific Company, 1112 Ruby Street, Spokane, Washington 99202
* **Wards Natural Science Establishment,** P. O. Box 1749, Monterey, California 93940
* **Wards Natural Science Establishment,** P. O. Box 1712, Rochester, New York 14603

122

ABOUT THE AUTHORS

Those chapters ending with "Nature and Science" were written by members of the staff of *Nature and Science* magazine.

James W. Atz is Associate Curator of Ichthyology at The American Museum of Natural History in New York City and lives in Port Washington, New York.

George W. Barlow is an Associate Professor of Zoology at the University of California, in Berkeley.

Raymond E. Barrett is Director of Education at the Oregon Museum of Science and Technology, in Portland.

Alan Mark Fletcher is a former science teacher who writes and edits science books. He has made several trips to South America to collect and study fishes and other aquatic animals.

Alice Gray is a Scientific Assistant in the Department of Entomology, The American Museum of Natural History.

Anthony Joseph teaches English at Macomb County College in Michigan, and has written many articles about science for children's magazines.

Barbara Neill has taught at children's museums in Connecticut and North Carolina. She is now Senior Instructor in the Education Department of The American Museum of Natural History.

Marlene Robinson is a science teacher and lives in Riverdale, New York. She has studied nature in the jungles of Cambodia, Thailand, and Vietnam.

Paul Showers is a member of the staff of the Sunday edition of the New York *Times*. He has written fourteen science books for young children.

Paul Villiard is a naturalist and free-lance writer who lives in Saugerties, New York. His most recent book is *Reptiles as Pets*.

David Webster is a teacher and writer who lives in Lincoln, Massachusetts. His books include *Brain-Boosters* and *Snow-Stumpers*.

Frank Wesley is Professor of Psychology at Portland State College, Oregon.

Nancy Kent Ziebur does experiments in plant breeding at the State University College of New York at Binghamton, and studies nature with her daughters.

Laurence Pringle, a former science teacher, is presently Executive Editor of *Nature and Science* magazine, published for The American Museum of Natural History by The Natural History Press. His writing and photographs have appeared in many magazines, including *Audubon, National Wildlife,* and *Natural History*. He is the author of two books—*The Only Earth We Have* and *Dinosaurs and Their World*—and edited *Discovering the Outdoors: A Nature and Science* Guide to Investigations of Life in Fields, Forests, and Ponds.

123

INDEX

126

Illustration Credits

All drawings, diagrams, and tables were prepared by the Graphic Arts Department, The American Museum of Natural History.

Laurence Pringle, pp. 13, 65
Herbert R. Axelrod, pp. 47, 96 (top)
John C. Goodwin, p. 25
Joan F. Goodwin, p. 23
T. F. H. Publications, p. 42
Anthony S. D'Agostino, pp. 96-97 (except 96, top)
Richard C. Helgeson, p. 112
Frank Wesley, p. 116
Paul Villiard, pp. 20-21
Courtesy of Bausch & Lomb, Inc., p. 51 (bottom)
Courtesy of Ward's Natural Science Establishment, Inc., p. 51 (top)
Courtesy of Education Development Center, pp. 102-104
Courtesy of The American Museum of Natural History, pp. 34, 38-39, 56, 60-61, 74